An
Anatomy
of
Kinship

Prentice-Hall Series in Mathematical Analysis of Social Behavior

James Coleman and James March, *Editors*

Flament *Applications of Graph Theory to Group Structure*

White *An Anatomy of Kinship:*
Mathematical Models for Structures of Cumulated Roles

PRENTICE-HALL INTERNATIONAL, INC. London
PRENTICE-HALL OF AUSTRALIA, PTY., LTD. Sydney
PRENTICE-HALL OF CANADA, LTD. Toronto
PRENTICE-HALL FRANCE, S.A.R.L. Paris
PRENTICE-HALL OF JAPAN, INC. Tokyo
PRENTICE-HALL DE MEXICO, S.A. Mexico City

An
Anatomy
of
Kinship

Mathematical Models for
Structures of Cumulated Roles

Harrison C. White

Assistant Professor of Sociology
University of Chicago

PRENTICE-HALL, INC.   ENGLEWOOD CLIFFS, NEW JERSEY

Library of Congress Catalog Card Number 63-13267
Printed in the United States of America. (C)

To my mother, Virginia Armistead White

Preface

Curiosity about variety in kinship systems led me to derive a catalogue of ideal types, confusion about their meaning then drove me to analyze the logic which underlay them, and it seemed only decent to compare ideal types with reality: such are the sources of Chapters 2, 1, and 3 respectively. Non-mathematical readers should have as much success as anyone with Chapter 1, for the notation is informal and the difficulties are conceptual and verbal. The penalty of our lifelong familiarity with kinship is the difficulty with which we learn to shed inappropriate connotations of familiar terms such as "father" when reading about non-Western societies. Just as the sociologist interested in the theory of social structure will focus on Chapter 1, an anthropologist curious to see if these elaborate models will do him any good should plunge directly into Chapter 3, which to a large extent can be read independently. A models man can turn at once to Chapter 2, which is self-contained. Mathematical maturity is more a state of mind than a level of training, and in principle it should carry any reader who remembers some algebra through Chapter 2. Many of the results in Chapter 2 can be understood without reading the text by examination of Table 2.3 and of the Figures, the code for which is specified in Fig. 2.6. Anthropologists also may find particularly helpful the categorization of second-cousins in Fig. 2.5 and the dissections of marriage among classificatory second-cousins summarized in Table 2.2 and earlier in Figs. 1.10 through 1.13.

My first thanks are due to colleagues who sustained during the fall of 1961 a pro-seminar on mathematical sociology where the core of Chapter 2 of the present book was evolved: Peter H. Rossi, Donald W. Fiske, O. Dudley Duncan, James A. Davis, Jack Feldman, Seymour Warkov, John Johnstone, Fred L. Strodtbeck, Karl E. Taeuber, Norman M. Bradburn, Robert L. Crain, and Judah Matras. Analysis of kinship structures using group theory was chosen as a topic because without extensive mathematical training one could in principle get to the frontiers of knowledge, and because it made evident the usefulness of mathematics for purely structural problems. The door was opened by two brief sections in *Introduction to Finite Mathematics* by J. Kemeny, J. Snell, and G. Thompson (Prentice-Hall, 1957).

A detailed commentary by David M. Schneider on a preliminary manuscript encouraged me to serious work on applying the models to reality. Suggestions and endless lists of references generously supplied by this bona fide anthropologist were moral armament with magic powers to assuage uneasiness over invading tribal domains with mathematics. It was only after I finished this book that I could understand Schneider's memos and thus see how much his comments had influenced my thinking.

Chapter 1 was stimulated by greater familiarity with the arguments among anthropologists about what classificatory roles meant and by an invitation to give a paper at the ONR Conference on Research in Formal Organization at the Carnegie Institute of Technology in June, 1962. Additional, more complex examples of three-dimensional lattices of cumulated roles will be found in my chapter in the proceedings of this Conference, edited by W. W. Cooper, to be published by John Wiley and Sons.

Of three short pioneer pieces on the mathematics of kinship discussed in the introduction to Chapter 2 one was never published and one is in French. Chapter 2 is based on, but by no means supplants, the three pieces. Messrs. R. R. Bush, A. Weil and C. Lévi-Strauss were kind enough to permit publication of their work as appendices. Thanks are due to my wife Cynthia A. White for translating M. Weil's chapter, to Mr. G. D. J. Edwards for checking the translation, and to the Beacon Press for permitting publication of the translation.

Some years ago exercises carried out by a student, Mr. Louis A. Perretta, whetted my curiosity about kinship models. Mr. Robert L. Crain checked the proofs in Chapter 2 and made valuable suggestions for clarifying the argument. A debt is owed to several women bold enough to type their way through thickets of fifth cousins and to the staff of the Social Science typing and reproduction pool. Financial support from the Social Science Research Committee of the University of Chicago is gratefully acknowledged. Thanks are due to Robert Carola of Prentice-Hall for his expert editorial work.

HARRISON C. WHITE

Contents

3 Models for Known Tribes   94

Additional References   150

Index   173

An
Anatomy
of
Kinship

Introduction

Primary roles can be cumulated into chains defining compound roles; for example, the sister of my father's father and the subordinate of my boss' protégé. Australian Aborigines build closed social structures of interlocked compound roles based on primary kinship roles, structures which are implicit in their laws and terminology and often recognized explicitly in part in their languages. Close analysis of the underlying logic and forms of Australian kinship systems is a necessary foundation for meaningful theories of function and change in these societies; also it should suggest ways to probe for homogeneous structures in our own society often obscured by a multiplicity of role frames, the size of the populations involved, and our commitment to hierarchic principles of organization.

One ego may group people in some structure of compound roles differently from another person taken as ego. If everyone is to agree on role obligations among a population there must be constraints on what set of primary roles can generate the structure of compound roles. Exponential proliferation of new roles must be reduced by laws of equivalence among compound roles so that the structure may serve a useful purpose in ordering social relations. That is, if a branching tree is used to represent the generation of new roles, nodes and branches in the tree should be coalesced in regular patterns. Finally, if the tree is not closed on itself but continues to "grow," it can represent, say, a field of friendship relations but not a closed social structure.

This constellation of problems is tackled informally in Chapter 1, where tree diagrams are the principal tool.

Structural mathematics is essential for an exhaustive treatment of structures of compound roles, because the combinatorial possibilities are too rich to keep straight verbally or even with diagrams. Abstract groups, matrices, and simple algebras will all appear in Chapter 2, where axioms define coalescence and closure for a set of primary kin roles. Types of structures are distinguished by what marriages are allowed among first and second cousins, as is the practice among the Aborigines, and a complete catalogue of distinct structures of each of four basic types is derived. Regulation of marriage choice is the most dramatic aspect of these kinship systems in action, to both natives and observers, and certain blood cousins in our sense are the leading examplars of the prescribed clusters of kin among whom, in a given structure, ego must seek his spouse.

A formal organization in our own society can also be regarded as a tree of cumulated primary roles, with the reciprocal relation of superior to subordinate usually the basic primary role. Such a tree terminates, by definition of the organization, at fixed numbers of branches away along various paths from a given member taken as ego. Normally one thinks of the organization as a structure of offices with fixed titles rather than a structure of roles with respect to an arbitrary ego. The models of kinship structures derived in Chapter 2, on the other hand, are homogeneous and closed; there are no terminal positions in the structure vis-à-vis the outside or at the ends of a hierarchy of authority. Yet the "clan" of kinsmen who are equivalent to each other in the structure constitutes a parallel to the office in a formal organization. These "offices" may be unnamed and not even fully recognized in an actual tribe conforming to one of the models, although usually a fixed name is assigned by the Aborigines to occupants of clusters of offices at least. Unnamed offices either in kinship structure or formal organization can be identified only by search for a set of groups of people who are equivalent in role rights and obligations relevant to the formal structure.

Formal explication of principles and ideal structures underlying the Aborigines' kinship systems should lead to many other insights and tools for penetrating beneath the everyday perceptions of our social structure which too often blind social scientists. Discussions at the end of Chapter 2 of structural duality, twisted generations, and the perception of structure in terms of exchange may provide useful clues. There is much more work to be done.

Australia is not the only area containing tribes with kinship systems approximating ideal models of closed structures. Islands neighboring Australia, and Burma, Southeast Asia, India, and South America each have some populations in which marriage is with prescribed types of classificatory kin. It is reasonable that a greater variety of systems closer to the complete consistency of ideal models should have developed in Australia. The Aborigines can be considered a distinct race who for at least hundreds of years before the English came had Australia almost to themselves to spread out in. Each horde in a small tribal population, with a simple hunting and gathering economy, identified itself over a considerable period with a fixed area surrounding its all-important water holes. Joint religious ceremonies brought tribes together and stimulated conscious formulations of their own kinship systems and adjustments to their neighbors', and individuals passed information as well as goods along extensive trading routes. Yet the population density was extremely low, probably less than one per square mile, and there was time and independence enough for the development of elaborate systems of intermarriage among the hordes of an area.

Anthropologists continue to argue about how Australian kinship systems might and do work. The literature of contention is as large as the literature of field reports, and both reach back into the last century. Brilliant verbal analyses are often coupled with ingenious models in the form of diagrams. Among the principal difficulties in using this literature are a lack of clarity and consistency in the operational meaning of the terms used by a given author and a lack of uniformity in terminology among authors. Data that are systematic, extensive, and precise are hard to find, and there remain few opportunities to observe systems relatively undisturbed by contact with whites. The how and why of a tribe's change from one type of consistent kinship system to another have been perennially fascinating questions; it is unfortunate that disintegration has displaced ordered change almost entirely. Probably many questions will never be conclusively answered. This book makes little reference to existing theories and interpretations by anthropologists, and it may be as well to divorce a fresh look at old problems from the existing rather polemical literature, but a great many of the individual concepts and results below are prefigured there. Existing theories, while possibly less rigorous and systematic than the analysis of ideal structures attempted here, treat the interrelation of kinship structure with other aspects of social behavior.

In Chapter 3 the major field report on each of several well-known tribes is analyzed to see what ideal model of a closed and consistent kinship structure best fits existing data. There is an excellent fit for some tribes, but for others it is clear that new kinds of models, more flexible and with less powerful assumptions about consistency, will be needed.

CHAPTER ONE

Roles, Kin Trees, and Homogeneous Structures

1.1. Introduction

A table of organization looks a bit like a family tree, with the president as great- ... -great-grandpappy and perhaps a clerk as great- ... -great-grandson. Brothers would be those subordinate to the same officer, such as vice-presidents to an executive vice-president. Often staff-line relations are indicated in the "T.O." by dotted lines, which vaguely suggest marital ties.

However, offices are customarily regarded as defining the formal organizations, with relations between persons derived from the nature of the offices they hold. And whereas in a bureaucracy in principle all members agree on the prescribed population of the organization, a family tree goes on and on until it fades out a certain distance away from whoever was the origin. Any analogy thus seems a weak one; besides, the family tree appears a rather pedestrian conceptual tool.

The theory of formal organization must have something to do with roles. It seems logical that a theory will be developed in which all role relations in formal organization can be taken as variants of basic types: for example, a trio of superior-subordinate, sponsor-protégé, and colleague-colleague roles. Yet, a similar categorization may apply in contexts other than organization, and certainly each specific variety of role found in a formal organization can be found outside. The distinctive aspect of roles in formal organization must be not their content but their articulation, the structure they form.

Existing role theory does not seem to be of much use with such large-scale problems of articulation.

Australian "section" systems, amazing feats of social engineering, articulate complex sets of roles into formal organizations. The methods of articulation can be revealed by an analysis of role terminology in the native languages. In principle the membership of the organization is prescribed instead of being variable with individual point of view. In a sense fixed offices are filled by individuals whose role relations follow from the nature of their offices. Yet these "section" systems are built out of kinship roles.

Clans are defined here as the set of mutually exclusive and exhaustive categories into which the population of a society is divided by kinship role relations. They may have concrete names but usually not. Marriage must always be outside one's clan (exogamy) and one's children usually are. The crucial point is that ego finds all partners for each kin role in precisely one other clan, so that we can well call such kinship systems prescriptive.

Homogeneity is the salient abstract characteristic of these prescriptive role systems. That is, the network of role relations involving one ego is identical in structure with that surrounding any other ego. In more concrete terms one can say that the genealogical prescriptions of potential spouses are the same for each (male) ego in the society. At first sight this might seem to eliminate section systems as possible analogies to bureaucracies. Yet bureaucracies too may have homogeneous structures in some sets of basic roles. Even the superior-subordinate role may cumulate into a closed chain if the head of the organization sees the ordinary worker level as the source of his authority. My view is that there will prove to be fundamental similarities between bureaucracies familiar to us and these complex kinship systems. The detailed kinship analysis to follow should suggest new and more sophisticated ways to view the structure of formal organizations in general. In addition to its value in taxonomy the analysis provides more basis for theories of evolution and change in formal organization.

1.2. Trees of Kin Roles

Brother and other relatives are social inventions, roles. A biological rationale is usually provided in a culture, but the criteria for assignment of one person to the role of brother to another *vary* from culture to culture in ways having nothing to do with biology. It is position in a structure of roles which perhaps most clearly distinguishes the kin role, say brother, from other roles with similar role behavior, say friend. To begin with, the brother role at once implies sister, father, mother, son, daughter, and wife roles. Some societies know not about the roles of brother and sister but rather think only in terms of roles for what we would call elder brother, elder sister, and younger sibling. Nonetheless, the familiar list above of seven kin roles "closest" to ego will serve as a convenient starting point.

Suppose a tribe is not so obliging as to use our English terms for the seven roles. Can one tell which is which without either concrete descriptions of role behavior or particular occupants as guides? Like other types of roles relevant to the structure of formal organizations, kin roles can be cumulated. Ego recognizes that each of his seven close relatives is his own ego with a field of seven kin roles, some of whose occupants will not be occupants of any of the seven roles closest to ego, and so on. Ego is prudent enough to allow for this in his terminology. For example, father's sister often will be a recognized role. The formal rules of cumulation can help to distinguish one role from another.

Brother's father will not be a role in a society without polyandry, nor will mother's husband be a role distinct from father. In a given culture the cumulation of kinship roles can be represented as a tree with fixed rules as to the types of branches that emerge from a given type of branch. A tree familiar to us can be specified as in Fig. 1.1 by the branching of each type of branch. Here the angle of a branch varies from highest to lowest for: Father = F,

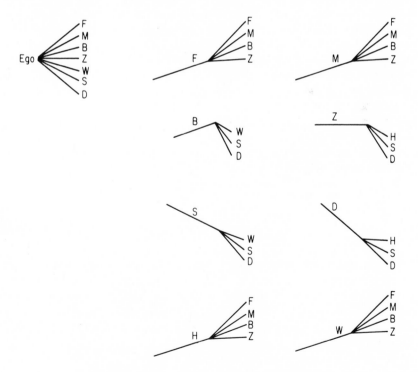

Fig. 1.1. Branching rules for a tree of kin roles familiar to Western minds.

Mother = M, Brother = B, Sister = Z, Wife = W, Son = S, and Daughter = D. It is not surprising, since ego was assumed male, that a new type of branch, for Husband = H, with its attendant branching rule had to be specified to fill out the cumulation of kin roles. Just as the Brother branch does not lead to a Father from ego's point of view in our kin system, so Sister and Son and Daughter do not lead to parents or Brother and Sister.

Already it should be clear that the lowly tree of kin roles is not such a dull affair. Try to work out the answer to this innocent question: how many cumulated kin roles does ego have at "distances" of 1, 2, 3, 4, and 5 branches from him? "Distance" must be in quotes since different branches, especially the marriage branch, hardly imply the same cultural or psychological distance.

If distance is arbitrary anyway one might as well replace two of the types of branch by compound branches. For example, Mother is Father's Wife and Daughter is Son's Sister. Since most societies emphasize patrilineal descent, F, B, Z, W, H, S are perhaps the most convenient minimal set of roles to use. We can sum up this reformulated tree in the new type of diagram of Fig. 1.2, for a Western kinship system in terms of one minimal set of roles. Ego (not shown) has a direct relation with all save the Husband role (if male), or Wife role (if female). For example, ego through his Father (F) has compound role relations with Father's Sister (Z), Wife (W)—i.e., ego's mother, Brother (B), and Father (F), as indicated by the arrows directed from F. Similarly, through FZ ego has compound role relations to FZH and FZS. In this notation, for example, FZ's daughter is FZSZ.

I have developed a number of other ways of representing the tree of cumulated roles for this example of a kinship system, but that given in Fig. 1.2 seems the most economical. Five branches lead out from ego, and at least two branches lead out from each node thereafter; so ego has at least $5 \cdot 2^{n-1}$

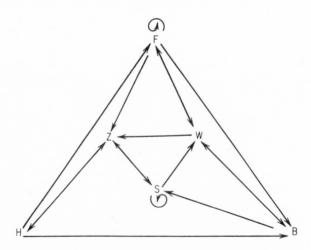

Fig. 1.2. Structure diagram for kinship role tree.

compound roles n branches away from him in the kinship tree drawn this way. It follows that the tree is too dense to be drawn in two or three dimensions save for small n. Before $n = 30$ there will be more branches in the tree than people in the world. Not all persons marry, nor do spouses always have at least two sons and two daughters; so for a particular ego there may never exist any person corresponding to most branches. For many compound branches there can be an enormous number of individuals filling that compound role with respect to ego. In our society multiple marriages, adoptions, etc. occur, but as yet these variations apparently have not been institutionalized as separate roles.

Members of an Australian society can understand cumulated kin roles of the sort constructed above and represented in a tree. In all societies some kin roles represented in the scheme of Fig. 1.2 by compound branches are given unique names and treated as unitary roles in some sense—e.g., our roles grandfather, mother, and daughter. A scheme such as that summarized in Fig. 1.2 provides a compact notation by which the analyst can identify kin roles in any observed system compatible with that set of minimal roles. There is an implicit assumption that any refinement of types of roles not made in the first step of the tree from ego will not be made thereafter.

1.3. People in Role Trees

Everyone is in principle kin to me is the fundamental rule ego assimilates in the primitive societies of interest here. It is difficult to delimit the population of one of these societies—or, for that matter, of any society—since often the "tribe" or "society" is more a matter of a convenient definition for the anthropologist than a sharp demarcation in the members' eyes. For the present, think of each society as an integrated unit totally separated from the world on an island. Australian "tribes" range in population from a few hundred to a few thousand.

Almost any kinship-role tree will have tens of thousands of nodes within a span of ten steps from ego, even if one counts only nodes whose occupants (if any) might be alive at the same time as ego. Most tribe members will each fill many different nodes within that span in the tree of a typical ego, even though many nodes will be empty of representatives and other nodes will have a great many. This may even be true for our society, but kin roles distant more than a few steps are normally ignored here. Our population is so great that the multiple nodes a stranger probably fills in my tree are likely to be many steps removed from ego, although we neither have nor could process the fantastic mass of data needed to obtain the relevant distributions.

Kin relations could be extremely confusing for ego in the small inbred society where he is trained to view everyone in a kin role, for there could be a bewilderingly large variety of roles vis-à-vis ego combined in a given person.

But compound kin roles are not imposed on the society by biological constraints; in some sense they have been institutionalized "by" the society as the primary means of defining and regularizing social relations among members. One would expect that in such societies kin roles are defined and compounded according to laws that have evolved so as to minimize ambiguity in role relations among concrete persons.

Consider a tribe through the eyes of one man taken as ego. He wishes to place the other members at the nodes of his tree. He perceives not only role relations they have to him but also role relations between them implied by their relations to him. A new role relation, say *alter*, describes the identity relation ego perceives between two persons in the same role with respect to ego; e.g., Mac and Sam, two father's brothers, have identical roles in ego's view.

If kin roles are to place the members of a tribe in a clear and mutually consistent structure of relations, the following properties are essential.

AXIOM IA. In the kin-role tree of a given person as ego, if two persons are alters in one node of the tree, then in any other node in which one appears the other must also appear as an alter to the first.

AXIOM IB. The tree of kinship roles must be such that all persons who are alters (have equivalent roles) with respect to one person as ego must be alters with respect to any other person as ego.

AXIOM II. If the same person can occupy two roles with respect to an ego, the content of the prescriptions of the two roles should be consistent (in the logic of that culture).

In principle, or as an ideal type, the Australian kinship system is one in which a consistent structure of social relations among members can be built solely on the basis of kinship roles as extended by a process of cumulation as in a tree. *Consistent* is the key word. Social relations mean norms, and the assertion is that social relations are consistent only if all members of the society agree when a norm is violated in a given instance. Whenever two persons considered identical in role by a third are differentiated by a fourth, there exists potential disagreement between the latter on the application of norms—the incest-taboo case below being an example.

In a consistent social structure based solely on kinship, application of norms governing role behavior must be homogeneous. Norms a person recognizes as governing a specific role relation of his with another person he can invoke as equally applicable to the mutual behavior of two other people whom he perceives as in that same role relation. Homogeneity in application of kinship norms is not relevant to the consistency of the structure of a society where the compounding of the kin tree is abandoned after a few steps. In such a society relations between members of different clusters of close kin are structured by other types of role trees or on different principles altogether.

A person may accept a stranger's definitions of the latter's relations with kin.

Important consequences flow from Axiom I, the two parts taken together. No male kinship role may be differentiated from a kinship role which would be related to the former as brother to male ego, nor may a female kinship role lead to a distinct branch for the role of sister to it.

One way to understand this axiom, as well as the general rationale of aboriginal kin systems, is to consider a hypothetical path of evolution. Early forms of the system of a given tribe are unknown and perhaps unknowable. The same system can emerge from different beginnings. Borrowing and imposition must have played some role, as well as conscious law-making. The kind of wear-and-tear with attraction toward improvements which presumably has a hand in language evolution should appear in the evolution of kinship systems, in which names for roles play such a large part. Since the real beginnings and evolutions of these systems are highly complex and largely unknown, and we are the ones who want to understand them, let's investigate in this and succeeding sections how a kin-role system familiar to us would have to be changed to fit the "needs" of a small Australian tribe.

Our kind of kinship tree (Fig. 1.1 or 1.2) does not satisfy the axiom. Consider the simplest possible case. John, Jim, and Joe are brothers. Then in John's role tree Jim and Joe are alters in the node for brother, but in Jim's tree John and Joe are alters. All three must view each other as alters rather than brothers according to Axiom I. The importance of the distinction is that alters do not generate additional branches in the kin tree.

Now consider a less inane case. Let the same three men each have a wife and a son. In terms of our kin-role tree John's son views Joe's and Jim's wives as alters, behavior toward whom is guided by identical norms. To Joe's son Joe's wife is, of course, mother (or father's wife, to be consistent in our terminology), whereas Jim's wife would be in the role of father's brother's wife. Obviously Axiom I is violated. The role Father must apply to all three men in the eyes of each son, and of course all three wives must be alters, to satisfy Axiom I. It remains to be seen why Axiom I is essential.

A man may not marry his sister, nor, equivalently, may a woman marry her brother. This word formula for an incest taboo is applicable in all societies, though the operational meaning varies. Obvious as it seems, the taboo has a curiously powerful impact in a society in which perceptions and acts are governed solely by kinship roles. Let the same three men's wives each have a brother and a sister recognized as such in our terminology. In John's eyes Jim's wife's brother is alter to Joe's wife's brother, as are the two wives' sisters. Necessarily in John's role tree the brother of Jim's wife is in the relation of brother to the sister of Joe's wife. Therefore to John marriage between them violates the incest taboo, but in either Joe's or Jim's eyes no such thing occurs.

Why, from a formal abstract view, is Brother so different from Son that the former role must be reduced to alter but not the latter? Some minimal roles, F, H, W, of the idealized tree specified in Fig. 1.2 can hold but one person with respect to an ego, whereas the other roles, B, Z, S, in the minimal set can hold an indefinite number of people. Axiom I requires that all initial plus compound branches hold at most one person or else all branches hold an indefinite number of persons with respect to ego.

The father role can be compounded with itself indefinitely, and the corresponding path in the tree specifies a single person at each node. The same is of course true of any path generated by repeated compoundings of the FW or mother role, or any path consisting solely of F links interspersed with single W links. (If ego is female the only difference is that there may be either F or H as the first link rather than either F or W.) F and H generate brother but not son roles from ego's viewpoint, which shows why the reduction of brother to male ego's alter throughout the tree is necessary to the validity of Axiom I, but not the reduction of son to male ego's alter.

Let us recapitulate the argument. Role trees generate role relations through the assignment of individuals to nodes. Each assignment of a person as ego defines a realization of the role tree; i.e., an assignment of each member to nodes. The unit of the structure of role relations is the set of relations between persons A and B in three distinct realizations of the role tree, those with A, B, and a third person C as egos. That is, a role relation between A and B is defined by the position of B in A's tree realization and of A in B's tree realization, whereas a structure of role relations is built on a unit of the comparison of a role relation with other members' perception of it. A path in a tree is an ordered sequence of branches of specified types. Each role in the minimal set defined with respect to ego in the tree, and only those, can be a branch from another node in the tree. Every relation, simple or compound, is defined by a path and vice versa. We now reach the basic condition: a structure of role relations is mutually consistent only if any path connecting a node containing A with a node containing B in one tree realization can be duplicated by a path connecting individuals A and B in each other tree realization; otherwise, not everyone would agree that the norm appropriate to the relation described by that path was applicable to the relation of A to B. But Axiom I is sufficient to guarantee this basic condition.

A stipulation is in order. Consider two compound branches in the kin tree which are given the same name in a tribe. They may nonetheless be recognized as distinct roles. In other words an occupant of one is not the alter of the occupant of the other, if the respondent who uses the joint role name for those two men is questioned as to the positions of the latter in the compound role tree. A near relative of the two men would certainly use different role names for them. Axiom I is not violated by such terminological inconsistency. It is unreasonable to expect kinship terminology in itself to reveal the full distinctions among roles a native draws where appropriate. His behavior toward distant relatives is not ordinarily governed by norms stringent and variable enough to require distinctive names in everyday usage for each distant compound role he recognizes. In Sec. 1.2 it was simply assumed that the rules for compounding branches were the same at all distances from ego in the tree. Now we can see that this uniformity is required by Axiom I rather than being a separate assumption.

There remains a basic ambiguity. Some role for brother or sibling of the same sex is institutionalized even in societies with kinship section systems; certainly such kin terms and role prescriptions are reported. Yet from the argument above centered around Axiom I it was concluded that brother could not be a distinct role in the tree of a section system. This conflict is resolved when kinship roles are differentiated into public and private aspects. Kin roles as cumulated into trees for section systems are not the total content of kinship relations perceived by individual members of tribes. These roles are only the public aspect of kinship relations, the aspect relevant in the eyes of tribe members to the places of individuals in the tribe as a whole. Exactly what concrete behavior patterns the tree roles regulate is an empirical question, but choice of marriage partners, through which new parts of the tree are identified, should clearly be one.

1.4. Reduction of Role Trees

One finding from the previous section is essential to the derivations which follow. In conjugating roles to form the kin tree for a consistent kinship system, brother is not a distinct role with respect to any male role nor sister with respect to any female role. That is, when it comes to assigning persons to a role tree consistent with a kinship section system, siblings of the same sex must be treated as alter egos. Thus men we would refer to as father's brothers are all assigned the role father, their sons are alters to ego just as are his "own" brothers, and so on. Anthropologists call this the principle of *brother equivalence*, and any system of kinship terminology consistent with it is called *classificatory*.

Given the above principle, the role tree can be greatly simplified. Throughout the role tree each female-role node can be paired with exactly one node which is related to the first as brother to sister. In the trees for Fig. 1.1 or 1.2 by contrast there are either two nodes which are in the relation brother to a given female-role node or two nodes sister to a male-role node, according to whether the role sex for the node the fewest steps from ego was male or female respectively.

One can now construct a simple tree of male nodes only. Define the new minimal set of male-kin roles for this tree as F = Father, S = Son, WB = Wife's Brother, and ZH = Sister's Husband. The branching rule corresponding to Fig. 1.1 is exceedingly simple. From each type of branch exactly three types of branches emerge: the forbidden branch is that which would undo the previous branch as a WB branch would undo a ZH branch, or an F branch would undo an S branch.

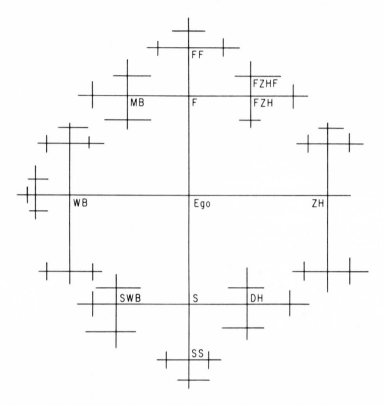

Fig. 1.3. Central part of kinship tree of compound male roles only, based on the principle of equivalence of siblings of the same sex. The node just left of each node stands in the relation of WB to the latter as ego; the node above stands in the relation of Father. The tree proliferates indefinitely, in principle. The positions of a few close relatives are indicated, for ego at the center.

It is natural to permanently assign one of four directions in a plane ($\pm x$ and $\pm y$) to each of the four types of branch. The first steps in a kinship tree of male roles appropriate to a section system are shown in Fig. 1.3. Observe that the form of this tree is necessarily unchanged if ego is taken to be in any other node than the one indicated.

If one implicitly associates with each node in Fig. 1.3 a node related to it as sister to male ego, then this tree is a complete tree uniquely specifying all distinct compound roles with respect to ego. The tree's structure diagram parallel to Fig. 1.2 is shown in Fig. 1.4. If desired the nodes for female roles can be regarded as located midway in each horizontal branch of Fig. 1.3. If in the eyes of ego a female-role node represents the sister role to the compound male role of the node to its left, then the male node to the right is in turn the husband role to the female role. If it is through the male node to the

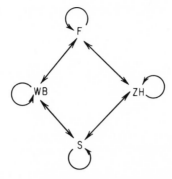

Fig. 1.4. Structure diagram parallel to Fig. 1.2, for tree shown in Fig. 1.3.

right of the female node that ego traces the path, then the female role is defined as wife to the role to the right, and the male node to its left is defined as brother to the compound female role. When the sex of ego in the role tree is taken as female, Fig. 1.3 can still be used with the origin point taken at a node for female role a half branch to the right of ego there.

The role tree in Fig. 1.3 has $4\,(3^{n-1})$ nodes n steps from ego. One's mother's mother's mother's brother, in our kin terms, is not a role of negligible interest to ego and yet it is six steps from ego. No more than six steps from ego there are 1456 nodes representing distinct compound roles, or about 3000 nodes if female roles are considered. Elegantly simple though its structure is, this general role tree appropriate to classificatory kin terminology proliferates too densely to be serviceable to ego without reduction.

Reduction can be viewed as coming about both through merging compound roles in the abstract and as a consequence of historical patterns in assigning persons to compound roles. By the analysis of the preceding section, when a person is assigned a new compound role with respect to an ego, say as a result of a new marriage, all other persons who are alters to the first person in any other role he occupied must also be assigned to the new compound role. The same set of persons must be alters in each role they occupy in the tree with respect to another ego. The population is thus divided into an exhaustive and mutually exclusive set of sections, the members of which are alters to one another in whatever roles they occupy with respect to any ego.

The rationale of the term *kinship section system* is now apparent. In Chapter 2 an axiomatic formulation of kinship relations among people in a system of sections is presented, mathematical machinery to describe it set up, and a fairly complete typology derived. There, in a sense, the derivation proceeds backward to find possible varieties of role trees from axioms stating the general properties of completely integrated section systems. Here reduction of role trees, usually short of a complete section system, through role merger is examined, and in the next section ways are examined in which complete systems might develop from such reduced trees under the impact of particular marriages in a society.

Cross-cousin marriage is a norm found in many societies. Suppose one male ego marries a woman in the role analogous to what in our conventional kin terms would be designated his mother's brother's daughter. In the convention adopted in Fig. 1.3 or 1.4 this male ego marries a woman in the role defined by the path with successive branches Father, Wife's Brother, Son, Sister, denoted hereafter by F(WB)SZ. A great many women in the society can be in that node who are not in our eyes "actual" mother's "actual" brother's "actual" daughter.

It is convenient to refer to the above marriage as MBD marriage, but it can be misleading. Mother's brother's daughter is simply easier for us to "place" mentally than F(WB)SZ. There is no ambiguity as long as a relative's designation in the symbols of Fig. 1.1, when used hereafter, is understood to refer to a node in Fig. 1.3, all such designations corresponding to the same node being understood to be entirely equivalent. Certainly each relative we can designate in the symbols of Fig. 1.1 is found in exactly one node in Fig. 1.3.

If then a man marries a woman who is MBD in the role-tree realization in which he is ego, it follows that the man is also assigned to the node for MBDH, or in the notation of Figs. 1.3 and 1.4 the node for F(WB)S(ZH). This means that all the other men who may have married an alter to that man's wife who are thus also F(WB)S(ZH) must be alters to that man. The role tree is still as in Fig. 1.3 but there can be no distinction in the roles of a possibly large group of men who appear as a group in a whole series of nodes including the ego node in the original man's tree, and for that matter in the same series of nodes in each realization of the tree in which any one of them is taken as ego. Similarly the populations of the WB and the F(WB)S nodes in that man's realization of the tree of Fig. 1.3 are identical. Suppose further that for all time any man in this society has married only his MBD. Equivalence of nodes with respect to the persons assigned to them snowballs rapidly. For example, any woman assigned to the MBD node of an ego is necessarily also assigned to the MMBDD node of that ego.

Let it be the law of the society, as well as an observed fact, that each man marries only his MBD. In other words, suppose that the roles W and MBD, or in the notation of Fig. 1.3 WB and F(WB)S, are defined as identical in that society. Already in Fig. 1.3 our roles Father and Father's Brother are taken as identical—i.e., men in one are alters of men in the other in the cumulative kin tree of such a society. This further step of equating W and MBD is not necessary to the consistency of the system, as defined in the previous section, but it is a norm found in many tribes.

If MBD and W roles with respect to any ego are indistinguishable, the general tree in Fig. 1.3 is reduced to a two-dimensional regular grid, shown

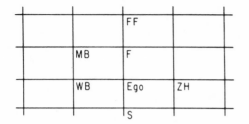

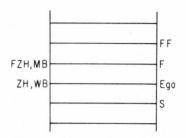

Fig. 1.5. Kinship role tree for which Wife role is indistinguishable from the role in which Mother's Brothers' Daughter is found. The tree continues to infinity in principle. Conventions as in Fig. 1.3, i.e., the node just above a given node is related to it as Father to Son, the node just to the left is related to its neighbor to the right as Wife's Brother to Sister's Husband.

Fig. 1.6. Male kinship role tree when W, MBD, and FZD roles are indistinguishable. A node is related to the node below as Father to Son, and a node is related to the other node at the same level both as WB to ZH and as ZH to WB.

in Fig. 1.5. A large number of nodes in Fig. 1.3 are lumped in each node of the grid. All of the $2(3^{n-1})$ nodes in Fig. 1.3 which are n or fewer steps away from ego must fit into the $2n(n+1)$ nodes in Fig. 1.5 which are n or fewer steps away from ego.

Suppose next that FZD, MBD, and W roles are all indistinguishable from one another. The tree is condensed still further to a simple ladder, shown in Fig. 1.6. Societies with this role tree can be called *bilateral cross-cousin marriage* societies, since one's wife is also both Mother's Brother's and Father's Sister's Daughter.

The patrilateral cross cousin of male ego is, in our terminology, Father's Sister's Daughter. If the roles of W and FZD are indistinguishable it can be shown that the general tree can be reduced to the same degree as when in Fig. 1.5 matrilateral cross cousin is identical with wife. The structure of the reduced tree is more complex, however. If it is to be isomorphic to a simple two-dimensional net a new convention must be used in the net, as shown in Fig. 1.7. Vertical straight-line paths each represent successive generations, Father to Son, as in Fig. 1.5. But where in one horizontal line a node is WB to the node on its right, represented by an arrow to the former from the latter, in the line above or the line below a node must be WB to the node on its left, and so on in alternation.

It is natural to ask what the reduced tree is when ZH and WB roles are indistinguishable, but each is distinguishable from both cross-cousin roles with respect to each ego. Instead of different branches of the general tree being folded over to touch, each horizontal straight line is shrunk to a single step, as in Fig. 1.8.

There are societies in which the role of Father's Father is indistinguishable from ego. Thus Son is indistinguishable from Father in ego's eyes. The reduced tree is the same as in Fig. 1.8, but rotated by 90 degrees so that horizontal becomes vertical, with the same conventions.

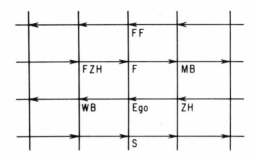

Fig. 1.7. Reduced kin role tree for which W and FZD roles are indistinguishable. The node just above a node stands in the role of Father to the latter. Each node stands in the relation of ZH to the node to which a horizontal arrow is directed.

If not only ZH is identical to WB but also Father is identical with Son for any ego, the reduced tree is extremely simple: a staircase, shown in Fig. 1.9. If further W is indistinguishable from MBD, the tree is reduced to a total of four nodes, or three roles distinct from ego, which can be called WB, MB, and F.

In other types of merging of roles the reduced tree can be extremely complex. There is no reason why it should be possible to draw any such reduced tree as a two- or three-dimensional lattice, even if very complex lattices are used. The tree in Fig. 1.8 obviously cannot be reduced to a lattice, for example.

Another important type of role identity arises from identifying the role of various second cousins with W. Anthropologists in their field reports single out MMBDD as the type of female second cousin most often regarded as preferred spouse. When the general tree is reduced by combining MMBDS node with WB node, with respect to every ego, the result is too complex and

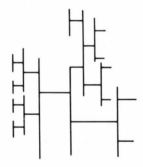

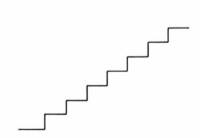

Fig. 1.8. Reduced tree when WB and ZH are indistinguishable. Each vertical line path continues indefinitely. Conventions as in Fig. 1.6.

Fig. 1.9. Reduced tree for ZH ≡ WB and also F ≡ S. The staircase continues indefinitely in principle.

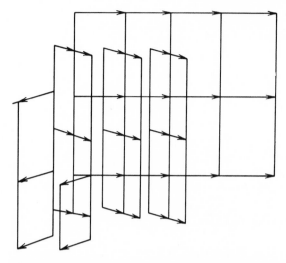

Fig. 1.10. Reduced role tree for the identification of FMBSD with W. Only a small fragment surrounding ego can be shown since branches proliferate so rapidly. Lines are slanted to indicate a new dimension as each plane splits off. Each node is in the role of ZH to the node to which the arrow goes in the same horizontal plane. As before, each node is F to the node directly below it on a vertical line.

dense to be diagramed. Let WB and ZH be equated as well as MMBDS and WB. Even then the reduced tree is so intricate that no attempt will be made to reproduce it here.

FMBSD marriage, on the other hand, corresponds to a role identification, FFWBSS with WB in the notation of Fig. 1.3, for which the reduced tree is readily visualized, though certainly dense. A fragment of this tree is shown in Fig. 1.10. To grasp fully the meaning of this as of the other diagrams one should identify familiar compound roles with a number of the nodes surrounding ego.

If, in addition to the WB role's being identical with FMBSS, WB is identical with ZH, the reduced tree can be written as a staggered plane grid, as in Fig. 1.11. This corresponds to a kind of bilateral second-cross-cousin marriage. First-cross-cousin bilateral marriage corresponded to the essentially one-dimensional ladder tree of Fig. 1.6. It is strange that anthropologists so heavily emphasize the MMBDD role when equivalence of FMBSD with W yields so much simpler reduced trees than identity of W with the former role.

A quite different reduced tree structure results if MMBDD and FMBSD are both identical with W and thus with each other for each ego, but WB is *not* identical with ZH, nor of course with any other second or first cousin. As shown in Fig. 1.12, the reduced tree is a staggered three-dimensional lattice.

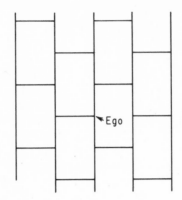

Fig. 1.11. Reduced tree for WB role identical both with ZH and with the second cousin role FMBSS. Each node is both WB and ZH to the node connected with it by a horizontal line, as well as F to the node directly beneath it.

A detailed analysis of the various possible sets of second cousins which can be equivalent to each other and to the Wife role is needed to clarify the relative significance of these various reduced trees. Mathematical notation is almost essential to carry this out; so it is postponed until Chapter 2.

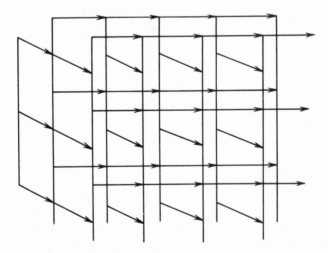

Fig. 1.12. Reduced kin role tree where the two second cousin roles FMBSD and MMBDD are equivalent to each other and to Wife role. No other second or first cousins are eligible as spouse. A three-dimensional grid drawn in perspective, it continues indefinitely in all three dimensions. Men at an arrowhead are WB to the node at the arrow's foot and are classificatory Fathers to the node below them.

MMBDS, FMBSS, ZH, and WB turn out to be the significant roles; the second-cousin marriage systems which are either empirically significant or structurally manageable correspond to reduced trees based on the equivalence of some combination of these four roles.

A fitting final example then is the reduced tree which results when all four of the above roles are identical; this is perhaps the role tree most closely analogous for second-cousin marriage to the tree in Fig. 1.6 for bilateral first-cousin marriage. In Fig. 1.13 this tree is shown: a four-sided column, each face of which is a ladder whose rungs are staggered with respect to those of its two neighbor faces.

In a tribe which conforms rigorously to the norms implicit in one of these reduced trees a man does not have to carry out elaborate calculations to place people in the proper classificatory relation to him. For instance, in a society with MBD marriage, how does a man know that a girl who is genealogically related to him as MMBDD is a potential spouse? He knows that any girl called sister by one of his MBD, real or classificatory, is alter to her and thus is classificatory MBD, and eligible as spouse. But his actual MMB is a classificatory brother to the FMB of any one of his MBD, and thus in her eyes his actual MMBD is classificatory W to her F. Hence any of the man's MBD will

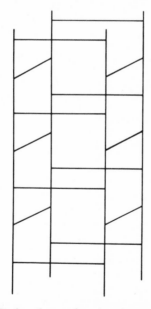

Fig. 1.13. Reduced tree for the closest analogue for second cross-cousins of bilateral first-cross-cousin marriage; i.e., WB, ZH, MMBDS and FMBSS roles with respect to any ego are indistinguishable. Compare with Fig. 1.6. Convention same as Fig. 1.11. This kin role tree continues indefinitely up and down and is a special case both of Fig. 1.12 and Fig. 1.11.

call his MMBDD sister and he need not perform any deductions to know that the latter is an eligible spouse.

A mathematician would call all diagrams in this section except Figs. 1.3, 1.8, and 1.9 linear graphs rather than trees. The general concept is the linear graph: a set of points connected by lines, no more than one line between each pair of points. A tree to a mathematician is a linear graph in which no closed loops of the line segments can be formed. Yet the kin-role tree can be regarded as an abstraction from the conventional genealogy in which kinship relations between named persons are specified, often in the form of a tree. Figure 1.3 regarded in this light contains closed loops; for example, the path to one of ego's father's brother's sons in his genealogy tree is condensed to the closed loop of going one step up and then returning one step down in Fig. 1.3.

If one does not look beyond the classificatory roles themselves, however, there is a basic difference between Fig. 1.3 and most of its reduced "trees." In the former there is exactly one nonredundant path between any two nodes in the tree, whereas in the latter there are an indefinite number and hence there are loops between the two nodes. A path is defined here as *redundant* if any branch in the tree is traversed more than once in the specification of the path. Corresponding to any number of nonredundant paths between two nodes there are a corresponding number of distinct designations of the kin relation between the nodes in terms of chains of classificatory roles from the minimal set for that reduced tree.

The original tree defined by the compounding rules in Fig. 1.1 can itself be regarded as the reduction of a general tree with seven branches at each node. Similarly Fig. 1.3 can be seen as a reduction of the tree of Fig. 1.2 corresponding to the equation of brother and sister roles with the alter or identity role. However, the reduction of Fig. 1.3 to, say, Fig. 1.5 cannot be phrased in terms of compounding rules, since these, like structure diagrams (Figs. 1.2, 1.4), cannot describe kin trees which contain closed loops.

1.5. Closing a Tree

With one exception all the examples of reduced kin-role trees in Sec. 1.4 have an indefinitely large number of nodes. In known societies with classificatory kinship systems only a limited number of roles in the reduced tree are used by ego to specify his relations to all members of the society—few enough so that all roles used may have separate names of their own rather than being designated by compounding several role names.

There are not an indefinitely large number of people in a tribe. Consider a tribe with the reduced tree in which MBS role is identical with WB role, shown in Fig. 1.5. Persons who are alive during any period of ego's life fill roles whose nodes are concentrated in a horizontal band around ego in Fig. 1.5. The width of this band is not confined to the five or six generations one might expect in view of human lifespans. If ego is the youngest son of a youngest son of a youngest son of a youngest son of a youngest son, then ego may be the same age as a man in a role many generations below him who is in a line of eldest sons from an elder alter of ego's great-great-grandfather. The principle is clear, although such extreme divergences are unlikely and the probability problems involved are extremely complex. In any case, there are, say, a thousand people in a tribe who must hold roles specified in a fairly narrow horizontal band around ego in Fig. 1.5.

As one moves left from an ego in Fig. 1.5, assigning other persons to roles they occupy, suppose one finds a node to which no person belongs. The cumulative effects of demographic variability—early death, sterility, etc.— would seem to guarantee this, although again the calculation of probabilities, even given good data, would be extraordinarily difficult. Go back to the node just to the right of the first node supposed empty. Whom did the one or more men who are alters in that last-filled node marry? Perhaps they didn't marry anyone, and thus had no children. Then move to the next node to the right and ask whom did their *sons* marry? Soon, unless the society is dying out, there must be a positive answer. One possibility is that men in a node left dangling on the left marry women whose brothers are in some node to their right.

In constructing the reduced tree nothing has been assumed about marriages between concrete persons. MBD role is identical with Wife role, but the girl who is Wife and MBD to, say, ego may also be attached to any other node of the tree. In Fig. 1.14 the reduced kinship tree is drawn again for a particular person as ego with X's at the nodes assumed above to have no people attached to them. A man named Jack assigned to node A is then assumed to marry a woman named Jill attached to node B, to take a simple example. But then by Axiom I all the men alters to Jack in the role of node A must also be alters to him in the role of node A', the role related to node B as ZH to WB. Jill is also attached to role B', hitherto assumed to have no persons assigned to it, since she is W to Jack; and all women alter to Jill in B are also alters to her in node B'. The process doesn't stop there. The Fathers of Jack and of his alters, assigned to role E, must also be assigned to role E', and the Mother's Brothers of Jill and her alters must be assigned not only to node G but also to node G', hitherto assumed vacant.

In principle, then, a reduced tree can be rolled up on itself as the result of a single marriage between a particular man and woman. There will be no nodes without people assigned, even in a small tribe: in Fig. 1.14 there will simply be an endless repetition of the same pattern of assignment of persons to nodes as found in the three columns containing and immediately adjacent to ego. In Fig. 1.15 this tree is drawn as a cylinder of three columns which suffices for the assignment of all members of the tribe to distinct groups of alters and for the portrayal of the closest paths of relation of each group of alters to each other group. More distant paths of relation between two nodes

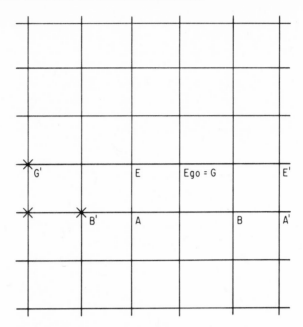

Fig. 1.14. Equivalence of nodes in the reduced tree of Fig. 1.5 established by identity of the persons assigned, in turn implied by the marriage of a man in role A to a woman in role B. (See text.)

can be defined in repeatedly circling around the cylinder. It is apparent that only kin roles in three lines of descent need be recognized by any ego in kinship terminology in order to uniquely distinguish all groups of alters.

In a real situation the classificatory logic would not be applied so inexorably as to require the complete roll-up of a tree as the result of a single marriage. It would be simpler to merely redefine the role of one spouse—say, John. All members of the tribe save his nuclear family of orientation may treat him after the marriage as a man with the role of node B' above by a sort of adoption process. However, if men in John's male line of descent follow up the initial marriage into the male line of descent to which Jill belongs, it seems likely that the tree would be rolled up in closed form as the cylinder of Fig. 1.15.

The three-line cylinder is so simple that the equation between nodes in the line of A and nodes in the line of A' might be an explicit norm. In other words, a society might have Fig. 1.15 as its reduced tree of kin relations in principle rather than as the consequence of a particular tradition of which concrete persons are to marry. The rule would be that not only is MBS role indistinguishable from WB role but also both are indistinguishable from the role of ZHZH. If John had married a girl attached to a node four or more columns to the right, however, it is not believable that the marital alliance between those columns which might become established historically would

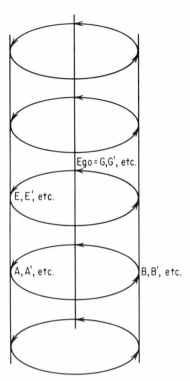

Fig. 1.15. The basic set of three columns in the reduced tree of Fig. 1.14 drawn as a closed cylinder. A man in one node is related as ZH to WB to a man in the node on which the arrow in that horizontal plane ends.

ever achieve the form of a norm stated in terms of kinship relation—the relation would be too distant.

In Fig. 1.15 as in Fig. 1.6 the effective reduced tree still proliferates indefinitely upward and downward. Consider another possibility for the marriage partner of John at node A in Fig. 1.14. Suppose he marries a girl Mary attached to the node P, shown in Fig. 1.16, which is two levels above A as well as two columns to the right. Earlier it has been shown why a girl in this role could well be the same age as John. By the same logic as before, John and his alters are also assigned to node A'; men in node K, in the relation of Father to them, are also assigned to node K'; and so on. If the logic of the classificatory system is applied relentlessly, all persons living, dead, and unborn in this tribe can be allocated uniquely to distinct groups of alters by the use of just three columns of classificatory kinship roles or terms. That is, just as Fig. 1.14 was effectively reduced to Fig. 1.15 so Fig. 1.16 is effectively reduced to Fig. 1.17, a twisted cylinder containing three vertical axes. Figure 1.17 would be the reduced tree of kinship roles in the tribe only in the unlikely event that there was a norm that FZHFZH was indistinguishable from WB and MBS roles.

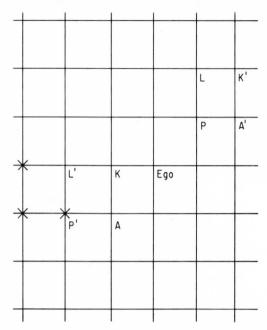

Fig. 1.16. Implications of marriage by a man assigned to node A to a woman assigned to node P. The same persons are assigned to nodes labeled with a given letter, whether primed or not.

There may be many men in role A; it may happen that one marries a girl of node P and one a girl of node B. Then, by Axiom I, girls attached to node P are also attached to node B, and conversely, since they marry men who are alters and thus both B and P girls are attached to the node B′ = P′. Similarly, all men in nodes K and K′ are alters to all men in nodes E and E′, or conversely. If this process of equating nodes is pushed to its logical conclusion, the result is that all men ever alive in the tribe can be divided into six nodes of alters, every other node in Fig. 1.16 containing exactly the same men as one of these six. This set of six nodes is shown in Fig. 1.18.

We have shown how a reduced tree of compound kin roles can be reduced further to a small closed set of linked nodes as in Fig. 1.18 solely as the result of historical patterns in the choice of wives by particular men. Figures 1.15, 1.17, and 1.18 do not represent the only compound kinship roles (nodes) recognized in principle as distinct in that kinship system; Fig. 1.14 does. Rather, they show the consequences of the fact that particular men, assumed to have been found in node A of the tree realization for some other man as ego (See Figs. 1.14 and 1.16.), have married particular women. These consequences flow from the basic logic of a consistent classificatory system in assigning men to roles, stated earlier as Axiom I. More complex reduced trees than that of Fig. 1.5, where MBS is the same as WB role, can collapse

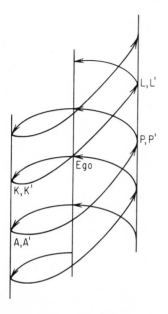

Fig. 1.17. The basic set of nodes in Fig. 1.16, drawn in the form of a twisted cylinder. All tribe members can be assigned to one of the nodes in this basic set. (See text.)

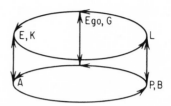

Fig. 1.18. If men in node A in Figs. 1.14 and 1.16 marry both women attached to node B and women attached to node P, then each man in the tribe is in a group of alters assigned to one of six nodes as shown above. A man is both F and S in classificatory terms to a man assigned the node directly below or above his, and he is in the relation of ZH to a man in the node on which ends the horizontal arrow (shown as curved line). Six classificatory kinship terms suffice to identify all men to ego as far as their position in the tree of compound kin roles is concerned.

in a similar way to small closed structures under the impact of particular traditions of marriage.

In the limit the closure of a reduced kin tree can result in a single node. Then all men are alters, and every man is in every conceivable compound kin relation with respect to ego. This would happen if one man married a woman who stood in the relation of Sister (Z) and an alter of the first man married a woman who stood in the relation of Father's Sister (FZ). A less extreme case is where all men are divided into two nodes which stand in the relation of WB and MB to each other—i.e., a man can marry any woman except those who stand in the relation of Z and FZ. In such degenerate cases the classificatory kinship system in its full rigor is almost pointless. People would revert to a less coherent system in which Axiom I is not applied fully or consistently.

1.6. A Catalog of Closed Systems

Through the consistent functioning of a classificatory kinship system a tribe can be divided into a small number of mutually exclusive groups of alters. Hereafter we refer to these groups as *clans*; they need not be the same as the "sections" or "clans" recognized by anthropologists. Men in a clan are equivalent to one another: each obtains a wife from the same other clan, finds his father in the same clan, his son in the same clan, and gives his sister in marriage to the same clan. Closure of the tree of compound kin roles, which was reduced to Fig. 1.3 by the principle of brother equivalence, can result from a set of explicit norms as to what roles are identical and/or from the implications of marriages between particular persons which flow from Axiom I. It matters little for the present functioning of a given system of clans how closure came about.

A fresh start is in order. One can formulate properties of clan systems as a set of axioms. From the axioms one can develop a formal algebra for such systems. Using the mathematical theory of representations of finite groups one can then derive all possible clan systems which have specified properties. It is natural to ask, for example, how many systems of n clans have the property that W is equivalent to MBD. Each such closed system can grow out of a reduced tree such as Fig. 1.5 as the result of a tradition of marriage between persons such as that summarized in Fig. 1.18.

In the next chapter this rather complex mathematical program has been carried out. All systems of a finite number of clans have been found that have one of the following properties:

I. Bilateral first-cross-cousin marriage.

II. Matrilateral first-cross-cousin marriage.

III. Patrilateral first-cross-cousin marriage.

IV. Simultaneous FMBSD and MMBDD marriage in which also brothers exchange sisters as wives.

In each case a subtypology is given, based in part on an exhaustive analysis of relations among second cousins.

In Table 2.3 of the next chapter the number of distinct systems of each of the above four types is given for each $n \leq 24$ and $n = 30$ and 32. This table should make clear the variety of clan systems possible. A weakness of anthropologists' analyses of data on existing tribes may be that they try to force the data into one of the very few systems of which they are aware. Sometimes tribe members are completely aware of the functioning of the actual system and give each distinct clan a name, but in most cases the existence and nature of the true system must be inferred from the structure of classificatory kin relations among tribe members living and dead.

A common opinion voiced in the literature [See, for example, A. P. Elkin, *The Australian Aborigines* (London: Argus & Robertson, 1948), p. 61.], is that the fourth type of system is the most common one among Australian tribes. If one were to assign equal *a priori* probabilities to each possible distinct system, assuming that each tribe independently "chose" a consistent system out of a hat through a trial-and-error process, the matrilateral first-cross-cousin systems should be the most common. It may be possible to develop a more refined model of *a priori* probabilities through considering in detail the processes described in Sec. 1.5.

Evolution of a clan system can proceed only in one direction—toward fewer clans—as long as people are classified only according to kinship relations in the closed tree. Persons who are alters in a given system can be distinguished only on some criteria external to the system. Right under the eyes of anthropologists some systems have been moving from fewer to more clans—from a less to a more complex closed tree. It is interesting that in at least one case the change has been consciously planned: one tribe with a simple system developed a feeling of moral inferiority with respect to neighbors with more complex systems and decided to learn about and put into effect a more complex one (See Sec. 3.6.) Such changes are complex, and a better system must be devised for handling intermediate states where kin relations and terminology are not as clear-cut and consistent as assumed in the axioms. Also, the difficult problem of the effects of intermarriage between different tribes, a common and even institutionalized practice, would have to be analyzed in treating evolution of systems.

Eight axioms stipulate the defining properties of any clan system in the mathematical analysis of the next chapter. One of these axioms does implicitly assert something about the evolution of a clan system. The axiom is that if a certain kind of relative is alter to ego in one clan, that kind of relative is alter to an ego in any other clan. This apparently innocuous axiom has enormous impact; without it the number of distinct systems of each type possible for any n would be exponentially greater than shown in Table 2.3. Yet this axiom seems arbitrary if one thinks of clan systems as appearing suddenly, say by agreement among a set of groups of men. However, if the system evolved along the lines suggested in the previous two sections it automatically follows that Axiom 8 is satisfied. Axiom I of this chapter implies the first five axioms of Sec. 2.2, and Axioms 6 and 7 are just definitions.

We have begun with the tree defined in Fig. 1.1, and our results may not apply to a kinship system based on a fundamentally different set of primary roles. The whole analysis has been informal. It should be possible to develop a mathematical framework for rigorously analyzing any tree of cumulated roles: the assignment of people to its nodes, its reduction and closure, all under a variety of assumptions about the kind and extent of consistency and homogeneity.

There is an enormous literature describing tribes with section systems, and a large literature on the proper interpretation of the data. Even those interested not in these systems as such but in getting ideas for analysis of other formal organizations should study this literature carefully. The analyses above and in the next chapter are only the skeleton of a full interpretation. Residence rules, authority patterns, religious behavior, descent rules, and a number of other characteristics of the tribe should be integrated with our formal models into a more general theory.

The reader now has seen that knowledge of kinship structure is not irrelevant to the study of formal organization; both depend on an understanding of the structure of roles, and even without much mathematical apparatus the systematic and careful use of formal tools such as trees can be rewarding.

CHAPTER TWO

Models of Kinship Systems with Prescribed Marriage

2.1. Introduction

Background. In 1949 André Weil, in the appendix to Part I of *Elementary Structures of Kinship* by C. Lévi-Strauss, sketched out one way to analyze in algebraic terms the structures of certain kinship systems. A basic step in his conceptualization is the assignment of all members of the society to a set of a few mutually exclusive and exhaustive marriage types, each husband and wife having the same type. (Each type reflects prescribed marriage of men in one clan to women in another.) He confines himself to systems with bilateral and matrilateral first-cousin marriage which further can be described in terms of cyclic groups. After mentioning that the theory of groups of permutations is applicable, he solves concrete examples through an ingenious and rather specialized use of the addition of n-tuples modulo two. Weil's work, translated from the French, is reprinted below, as Appendix 1.

R. R. Bush in an undated mimeo manuscript proposed permutation matrices as a more convenient tool for the analysis. Like Weil, Bush carries out the analysis in terms of marriage types, although the implications for clan membership are always drawn by both authors. Bush suggests that $(M!)^2$ societies with M marriage types are possible, and he works out a few concrete cases for small M. Appendix 2 is a reproduction of Bush's work.

Kemeny, Snell, and Thompson develop the work of Weil using the tool suggested by Bush. In Secs. 10 and 11 in Chapter 5 of *Introduction to Finite Mathematics* they develop the elementary properties of groups and subgroups of permutation matrices; then in Secs. 7 and 8 of Chapter 7 they present a reformulation of the Weil analysis. Although their book can be called an elementary text, these brief sections, with their extensive problem sets, are a major advance over the previous work. The properties of the societies to be investigated are formulated as an integrated set of axioms. The seventh and last axiom, which postulates a kind of homogeneity in the kinship structure, is not foreshadowed in the work of Weil and Bush. Using this plausible axiom they show there are only a few allowed societies with a given number of marriage types.

Content. In this chapter we systematically derive and describe all distinct kinship structures which satisfy the Kemeny-Snell-Thompson axioms and exhibit one of several kinds of prescribed marriage of particular interest to anthropologists: bilateral, matrilateral, and patrilateral first-cross-cousin marriage, and marriage in which wives are exchanged between pairs of clans. A simple type of graph is used to depict the results for cases typical of each subtype defined for each of the four major classes of kinship systems.

A considerable reformulation of the Kemeny-Snell-Thompson approach was desirable. Marriage type is not a concept to be found in the field notes of anthropologists or the thinking of members of the societies. It is not only possible but also proves to be simpler to define the permutation operators in terms of clans. Instead of having one matrix represent the transformation of parents' marriage type into son's type, and another similar matrix represent daughter's marriage type, we deal with one matrix for transforming husband's clan into wife's clan, and another for transforming father's clan into children's clan. Both the formulation and the results are easier to interpret concretely, and the derivations are somewhat simpler.

We show that any abstract group, or equivalently any group of permutations, which can be generated by two elements corresponds to at least one allowed society. Moreover, we find that the regular matrix representation of an abstract group, which is easily written down from the multiplication table, provides a convenient translation of the results of the abstract algebraic derivations into the explicit matrix operators in terms of which the societies can be visualized. However, the same abstract group can represent not only distinct societies but also different types of societies. It is much simpler to consider not groups but pairs of generators of groups in deriving all possible societies of a given kind. Even then it is necessary, after defining what is meant by distinct societies, to show that each allowed pair of generators found yields a distinct society.

The reformulation is worked out in the following three sections. In the fifth and sixth sections first- and second-cousin marriages are treated exhaustively to provide a clear basis for distinguishing major types of societies. In Secs. 2.7–2.12 the derivations are carried out and societies of each type counted.

Additional tools for analyzing these societies are developed in the remaining sections. In the three earlier works cited, the primary question asked for a given society or type of society was: which of his female relations can male ego marry? A second question, which can be answered using the results of this chapter, is: what different kinds of relationship can exist between the same two persons in a given type of society? Since there are few clans relative to the number of people, and since everyone in the society is by hypothesis related to some degree, obviously a large number of distinct relationships must relate any pair of people. Two important special cases treated in some detail are the conditions under which (1) two persons can be bilateral cross cousins of the same degree and (2) second- and first-cousin relations of various kinds can coexist between the same two people. The ambiguities inherent in applying Western kinship terms to classificatory systems are analyzed at the same time. The meaning of generations, alternative ways of visualizing marriage as exchange, and abstract similarities among societies with different descent rules are also investigated with the additional tools.

Applications. One important use of this type of analysis can be clarification and simplification of the sheer classification and description of the many rather complex kinship systems thought to conform in principle to the axioms. In order to use the results of this chapter to classify existing societies, some transcription of conventional anthropological terms—which are not entirely uniform and unambiguous—into the terms defined here is necessary, as will become clear in Chapter 3. *Clan* as we use it is the largest group of persons in a tribe who follow the same preferential marriage rule with respect to other clans.

The more interesting question is how to use formal analytic results such as these to help answer theoretical questions of substantive importance. The only satisfactory answer is the detailed report of a successful application. Some comments on the direction of future work using these analytic results may be instructive. In *Marriage, Authority, and Final Causes* (The Free Press, 1955) Homans and Schneider take issue with Lévi-Strauss' explanation of the predominance among societies with unilateral cross-cousin marriage of the matrilateral form. It would seem logically desirable when evaluating these explanations to consider all possible societies of each type in comparison with all the possible examples of the other type. First, the data on such societies cannot be complete, since the world has not long been blessed with anthropologists. Second, it is necessary to explain why some subtypes of matrilateral marriage societies are rare at the same time as one attempts to explain why patrilateral marriage societies are less common than matrilateral ones, if the explanation is to be convincing. If there is a "larger" population of distinct matrilateral than of distinct patrilateral systems in some relevant sense, one can argue that matrilateral societies are more common partly because of a chance search process "by" a society for a stable, consistent system of prescribed marriage.

G. P. Murdock in *Social Structure* (Macmillan, 1949) proposes a rationale for the evolution of societies from one type of kinship system to another. He relies heavily upon the classificatory aspect of kinship terminology. It seems possible that the formal analytic results reported here can be used to clarify and revise some aspects of his analysis. To this end one could explore the plausibility of various formal measures of the closeness of different prescribed marriage systems. Not all the pushes and drags influencing change in a social system can be described by reference to the dynamics of behavior among pairs or small groups of relatives, and our formal analytic results provide one way to consider the properties of the system as a whole. In some ways the system presented below predisposes the user to think in terms of macro-effects, or what Homans and Schneider term "final" causes as opposed to the "efficient" causes the latter find in interpersonal dynamics.

Methods. An attempt has been made to keep the mathematical approach as simple as possible. In any case most of the usual apparatus of applied group theory has not proved very helpful. A brief guide to some of the relevant mathematics has been included in the form of a bibliographic note.

The chapter digit 2 in our decimal notation for figures will be suppressed for figures in Secs. 2.7 through 2.16 since so many figures and cross references among them are necessary there.

2.2. Axioms

We wish to construct a typology of all prescribed marriage systems that have the following properties:

1. The entire population of the society is divided into mutually exclusive groups, which we call *clans*. The identification of a person with a clan is permanent. Hereafter n denotes the number of clans.

2. There is a permanent rule fixing the single clan among whose women the men of a given clan must find their wives.

3. By rule 2, men from two different clans cannot marry women of the same clan.

4. All children of a couple are assigned to a single clan, uniquely determined by the clans of their mother and father.

5. Children whose fathers are in different clans must themselves be in different clans.

6. A man can never marry a woman of his own clan.

7. Every person in the society has some relative by marriage and descent in each other clan: i.e., the society is not split into groups not related to each other.

8. Whether two people who are related by marriage and descent links are in the same clan depends only on the kind of relationship, not on the clan either one belongs to.

We also refer to these eight properties as axioms.

2.3. Marriage and Descent Rules as Permutation Matrices

The rule required by Axioms 2 and 3 can be presented in the form of a permutation matrix of side n: i.e., a square matrix with exactly one entry of unity in each row and column and all other entries zero. Number the clans from 1 to n, and let the ith row and the ith column of the matrix correspond to the ith clan. Assume each row of the matrix corresponds to a husband's clan, the wife's clan being identified with the column in which the number 1 appears in that row. Call this matrix W. It shows the one clan from whom women of any given clan get their husbands and the one clan from whom the men of any given clan get their wives. Note that polygamy and/or polyandry are consistent with the axioms, though for simplicity we speak in terms of monogamy.

Since the wife's clan is uniquely determined by her husband's clan, the clan of a couple's children can by Axiom 4 be uniquely specified by the father's clan. Let C be the permutation matrix in which $C_{ij} = 1$ if fathers of clan i have children of clan j. C must be of the form of a permutation matrix since, by Axiom 5, children in any given clan have fathers in only one clan, as well as vice versa.

There are $n!$ possible permutation matrices, or altogether there are $(n!)^2$ combinations of marriage and descent rules for societies with n clans which have the first five properties. Many of these combinations violate Axioms 6, 7, and 8, and only a small fraction of the valid combinations of rules are structurally distinct. It is necessary to define the latter term precisely in order to count and group distinct structures, but first we must study the implications of Axioms 6, 7, and 8.

W and C not only look like matrices but also can be meaningfully combined by the operation of matrix multiplication. For example, consider the element $(WC)_{ij}$ in the ith row and the jth column of the matrix WC formed by multiplying the matrices W and C in that order. By the standard definition of matrix multiplication,

$$(WC)_{ij} = \sum_{k=1}^{n} W_{ik} C_{kj}.$$

There is exactly one unity in the ith row of W: say it occurs in the p column. Similarly in the jth column of C there is only one unity, say in the q row; so the sum on the right in the equation above is zero unless $p = q$ in which case the sum is just unity. In words this means the (i, j) element in (WC) is unity if and only if men in the ith clan marry women whose clan brothers are the fathers of children of clan j. But there must exist some j such that $C_{pj} = 1$, by Axioms 5 and 4. To put it affirmatively, the matrix (WC) specifies for a man of each clan the clan to which the children of his wife's brother belong. Any ordered series of any powers of W and C when multiplied together will, by the same logic, give a product matrix which is a permutation matrix specifying for each possible clan of a man the clan of a given relative of his.

One possible product matrix is the identity matrix, call it I, in which $I_{ij} = 1$ if and only if $i = j$, with all other elements zero. Whatever the clan of a man, any relative of his for whom the product matrix is I will have the same clan that he does. Axiom 6 requires that in the matrix W no diagonal element W_{ii} be unity; certainly W cannot be the identity matrix I. Approximately $n!/e$ (where $e = 2.71 \ldots$) $n \times n$ permutation matrices satisfy this restriction. C on the other hand can be I when the children of men of any clan are in that clan. If any diagonal element of C is unity, all C_{ii} must be unity, for otherwise some men would be in the same clan as their children but not others, in contradiction of Axiom 8. A parallel argument leads to the conclusion that any product matrix formed from W and C must have no diagonal elements unity or else it must be I.

Axiom 8 has further implications. If any man is in the same clan as his own son's son all men must be; so $C^2 = I$, and so on. If none of the powers $C, C^2, C^3, \ldots, C^{n-1}$ are the identity matrix, then C^n must be. For suppose $C^i \neq I$, $i = 1, \ldots, n$. Then each succeeding generation of sons of sons has a clan different not only from the clan of the man we started with but also from all clans of intermediate ancestors in the male line, given Axiom 8. Thus there must be $n + 1$ clans, in contradiction to our assumption in Axiom 1. So $C^p = I$ for some $1 \leq p \leq n$. Thus any power of C is equal to C to a power between 1 and p, inclusive. The same conclusion obviously can be drawn concerning the powers of W and the powers of any product matrix which is made up of W and C, since any product matrix corresponds to a relation of a fixed kind.

The inverse of a matrix M is defined by

$$MM^{-1} = M^{-1}M = I.$$

For example, C^{-1} is the matrix which specifies for each clan a son may have what clan his father is in. Thus $(C^{-1})_{ij} = C_{ji}$. Suppose C is of order p; i.e., p is the lowest integer such that $C^p = I$, where it was shown above that $p \leq n$. Since $CC^{p-1} = C^p = I$, the inverse of C can also be written as C^{p-1}; and similarly for W and for any product matrix. Thus C and W and their product matrices can be used to describe the change in clan in moving from a given person to his ancestors as well as to his descendants. Thus to every possible relation of a person in the society there corresponds a matrix which is some product of repetitions of C and W. We will often use M as a general symbol for such a matrix and call it a *relation matrix*.

There is a final very general restriction implied by Axiom 8 together with Axiom 7. If we calculate the product matrices formed by each of two different sequences of W and C matrices, we often find these two product matrices are equal; i.e., the ones and zeros appear in the same places. Let us arbitrarily designate the distinct matrices which result from multiplying W and C in all possible orders and combinations by the symbols A_1, A_2, A_3, ... There are exactly n such matrices, as is clear intuitively since one ego has only n essentially different kin relations, one with persons in each of the n clans, and Axiom 8 requires the structure to be homogeneous.

Axiom 7 states that for any pair of clans k and j there is one of the matrices A_i in which the k, j element is unity. A given matrix A_i has only one unity entry in a row k; there must be at least n matrices A_i. Suppose there is an additional one, A_{n+1}. Then in A_{n+1} the kth row must be identical with the kth row in some A_i, $i \leq n$. The kth row of A_{n+1} can be used to specify what the clan is of some one kind of relative of a person in clan k, and similarly for A_i. But two persons related in specified ways to a given person also have a specified relation to each other, and here these two persons are in the same clan. It follows that A_i and A_{n+1} must be equal in each row, for otherwise Axiom 8 is violated. In other words, if two of any set of permutation matrices satisfying Axioms 7 and 8 are equal in one element they are identical. There are therefore exactly n distinct permutation matrices generated as products of any W and C matrices for a society with n clans which has properties 1–8.

There is at least one society satisfying all eight axioms for any n: that with $C = I$, and $W_{i,i+1} = 1$, $1 \leq i < n$, $W_{n,1} = 1$, and all other $W_{i,j} = 0$. The n distinct matrices are W, W^2, . . ., W^{n-1}, and $W^n = I$. Another obvious possibility is a society with $C' = I$, $W'_{i,i+2} = 1$, $1 \leq i < n-1$, $W'_{n-1,1} = 1$, and $W'_{n,2} = 1$, and all other $W'_{ij} = 0$; again W', $(W')^2$, . . ., $(W')^n$ are the distinct matrices. It is intuitively clear that this second society differs from the first only as to the numbering of the clans.

We will use this description of societies by permutation matrices to classify the societies according to what kinds of relatives are allowed to marry. It is natural to say that two societies described by different pairs of C and W matrices are structurally distinct if and only if there is at least one kind of relative who is allowed to marry ego in one society but not the other. Let $M(C, W)$ be any matrix defined as a product of a sequence of powers of C and W. Then two societies have equivalent structures when $M(C, W) = W$ in one if and only if $M(C', W') = W'$ in the other where M has the same form in both. In the example above $M(C, W)$ can be written as W^m. If $W^m = W$ then $m = jn + 1$ for some integer j. But $(W')^n = I$ also; so $(W')^m = W'$ if and only if $W^m = W$.

Very restrictive conditions thus must be satisfied by the C and W matrices. Many fewer than $n!$ ($n!/e$) pairs of permutation matrices satisfy these restrictions, and even fewer pairs give structurally distinct societies. However, there is no simple way to count the number of distinct societies with properties 1–8. We shall consider only certain general classes of our ideal-type societies. These classes will be defined by the kinds of first-cousin marriages which are allowed in known primitive societies. To simplify the derivations we need to develop a more abstract view of the A_i matrices.

2.4. Groups and Societies

Consider the n distinct relation matrices A_i generated by a C and a W matrix for a society with n clans which satisfies Axioms 1–8. The product of A_i and A_j is some A_k for any i and j. We also proved above that one of the A_i is the identity matrix and that for each A_i there is an A_j which is its inverse. Matrix multiplication is associative; i.e., $A_i(A_jA_k) = (A_iA_j)A_k$, which is another way of saying, for example, that a man's son's grandson is the same person as his grandson's son. Therefore the set of A_i's constitute a representation of an abstract group. A group is specified by its multiplication table, in which the entry in the ith row and jth column is a_k when $a_ia_j = a_k$.

In the appendix to this chapter we go a step further and show that a regular representation of *any* abstract group generated by two elements constitutes a set of A_i describing an allowed society. The number of elements in the group is called its *order*. One way to begin classifying societies would be by examining all instances of abstract groups of different orders. There is a well-organized and highly developed literature on the properties of abstract groups in which all groups of order less than, say, 32 are examined in exhaustive detail. Unfortunately this approach is not fruitful, for there are usually numerous pairs of elements in a group which will generate the group. Thus the same group can be isomorphic with the set of distinct relation matrices for two very different societies.

It is more efficient to begin by finding all pairs of abstract group generators C and W which have specified characteristics for a given group size n. Then one can construct their regular representation from the multiplication table and diagram each society. These calculations are much simpler because we can treat C and W and their products as elements in an abstract group algebra rather than as explicit matrices. Once the multiplication table showing all possible products of C, W, and the other $n-2$ distinct elements is derived, one can write down a concrete matrix for each element. The $n \times n$ permutation matrix which sends the standard list of elements (the row or column headings of the multiplication table) into the ith row of the table is a valid matrix representation of a_i. (See the appendix at the end of this chapter.) It was proved that there are the same number of clans as elements, and the numbering of the clans is arbitrary; so the matrix representation obtained from the group multiplication table uniquely specifies a society, as long as C and W are explicitly identified in the list of elements. The next step is to winnow out those representations of C and W, if any, which do not give rise to marriage conditions different for at least one type of kin relation from the marriage conditions required by societies already included. Later a graph notation for describing the society more succinctly than by its W and C matrices will be presented.

2.5. First-cousin Marriages

It is both logically and empirically appropriate to classify kinship systems on the basis of the kinds of first cousins allowed to marry. There are four possible kinds of first cousins, if one is male and one female. These can be described most easily by a family tree, in which the symbolic convention is:

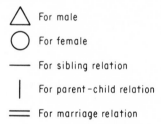

The arbitrary convention of referring all relations to a male ego will be used throughout. When the girl cousin is the male's father's brother's daughter the relation graphically is as shown in Fig. 2.1; this girl cousin is written FBD as earlier. When the two siblings who are parents of the first cousins are of the same sex the latter are termed *parallel* cousins, otherwise *cross* cousins. When the parent of male ego is female the cousins are said to be *matrilateral* cousins; male ego and the girl are *patrilateral* cousins if it is the father of male ego who is a sibling of one of the girl's parents. In Fig. 2.1 the boy and girl are patrilateral parallel cousins. When the father of the boy is the brother of the girl's mother and also the mother of the boy is the sister of the girl's father they are said to be *bilateral* cross cousins.

A fundamental question to be answered is: what kinds of relations can marry in a society specified by given C and W matrices? Begin with Fig. 2.1. The matrix $C^{-1}C$ specifies in a row i by a unity entry the column for the clan of the girl who is a patrilateral parallel cousin of male ego in clan i. The clan of the boy's father, say j, is specified in the ith row of C^{-1}, the father's brother is in the same clan, and the latter's children are in the clan specified in the jth row of C, that is in the clan specified in the ith row of $(C^{-1}C)$. In this case it is easy to see directly from Axioms 2–5 required for all societies

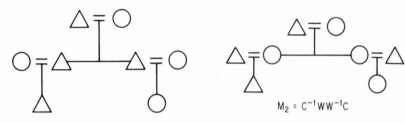

Fig. 2.1. Patrilateral parallel cousins.

Fig. 2.2. Matrilateral parallel cousins. M is the relation matrix, in which the girl's clan is specified by the column in which a unity entry appears in the row specified by the boy's clan.

considered here that the boy and girl cannot marry, and $CC^{-1} = I$, as it should.

If a boy can marry a girl, her clan must be that indicated by a unity entry in a row of W corresponding to the boy's clan. In symbolic terms, if M is the matrix describing the clan of a girl relation of male ego (for Fig. 2.1, $M = C^{-1}C$), then

$$M = W$$

is the condition that must be satisfied if the girl is to be a legitimate marriage partner of the boy, whatever his clan. By Axiom 6, $W \neq I$, ever, so in no society satisfying Axioms 1–8 can a boy marry his female patrilateral parallel cousin.

Marriage between matrilateral parallel cousins (see Fig. 2.2) is also forbidden, since there

$$M = C^{-1} W W^{-1} C$$

or $M = I$, using the associative law. Just as the conversion of husband's to wife's clan is specified by W, the conversion of wife's clan to husband's clan is given by W^{-1}.

The other two kinds of cousins, matrilateral and patrilateral cross cousins, can marry for some W and C matrices. (See Figs. 2.3 and 2.4.) Matrilateral cross cousins can marry if and only if

$$W = M = C^{-1}WC.$$

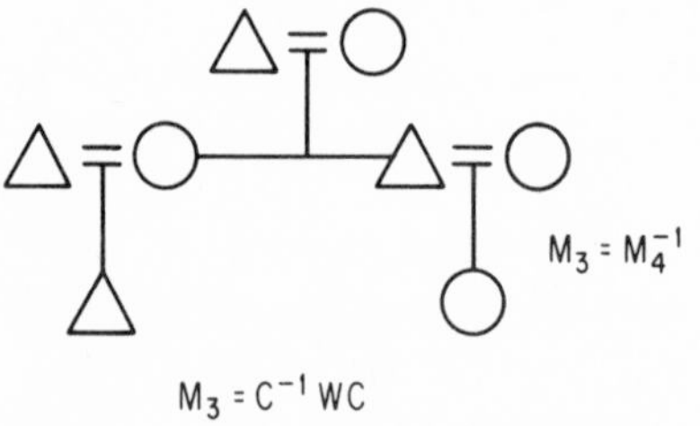

$M_3 = M_4^{-1}$

$M_3 = C^{-1}WC$

$M_4 = C^{-1}W^{-1}C$

Fig. 2.3. Matrilateral cross-cousins.

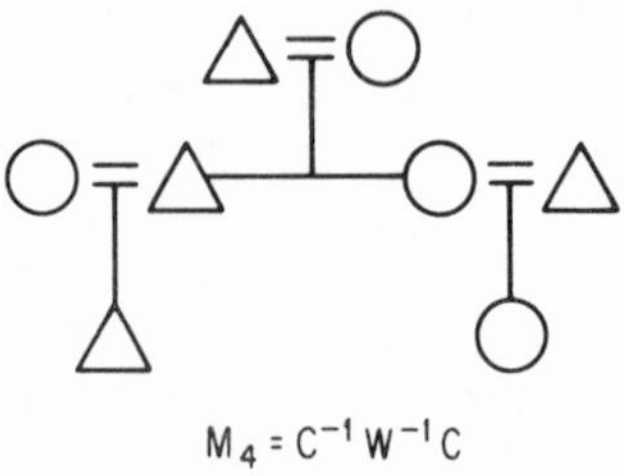

Fig. 2.4. Patrilateral cross-cousins.

If we premultiply both sides of the equation by C, we have $CW = (CC^{-1})WC$, or

$$CW = WC$$

as the necessary and sufficient condition. In other words, the order in which W and C are multiplied does not affect the product matrix; i.e., W and C commute. Since all relation matrices are generated as products of W and C it follows at once that all n distinct matrices A_i for a given society must commute with each other if matrilateral cross-cousin marriage is allowed.

Male ego is allowed to marry many other kinds of relations than matrilateral cross cousins in a society described by a commutative group of matrices, and there are several different subtypes of such societies. The first major goal will be to specify and analyze all such societies. It proves more orderly to define subtypes by simple algebraic conditions on C and W than by what other types of relatives marry.

From Fig. 2.4 it can be seen that patrilateral cross-cousin marriage is allowed if and only if

$$W = M = C^{-1} W^{-1} C.$$

Again premultiplying both sides of the equation by C we have

$$CW = W^{-1}C$$

for the necessary and sufficient condition. This can be called the semicommutative condition. An alternative form is obtained by first postmultiplying both sides of this equation by W^{-1}:

$$C(WW^{-1}) = W^{-1}CW^{-1} \quad \text{or} \quad C = W^{-1}CW^{-1},$$

and then premultiplying both sides by W:

$$WC = CW^{-1}.$$

The second major goal is to identify and describe all societies in which this equation holds, and for each to find what kinds of relatives can marry.

There is an ambiguity in our categories of cross-cousin relations. Cousins may be bilateral; if they are cross cousins then both Fig. 2.3 and Fig. 2.4 describe the relation of male ego to his girl cousin. In a society in which bilateral cross cousins may marry, both $WC = CW$ and $CW = W^{-1}C$ must apply. But then

$$W^{-1}C = WC,$$

if we combine the two equations. If we postmultiply by C^{-1}, then

$$W = W^{-1}$$

is a necessary condition for bilateral cross-cousin marriage. An alternative form is

$$W^2 = I;$$

i.e., the order of W must be two.

Furthermore, bilateral cross cousins cannot exist in a society unless $W^2 = I$. From Fig. 2.3,

$$M = C^{-1} WC$$

must describe the girl's clan by columns for the boy's clan by rows; but by Fig. 2.4,

$$M = C^{-1} W^{-1} C$$

must also describe this transformation of clans. A given girl can be in only one clan; so

$$C^{-1} W^{-1} C = C^{-1} WC$$

is required if there is not to be a contradiction. But this can be reduced to the equation $W = W^{-1}$.

On the other hand, in any society there can be bilateral parallel cousins. Both in Fig. 2.1 and Fig. 2.2 the relation matrix between the boy and girl cousins is just the identity. Bilateral parallel cousins can never marry but can exist in any society; bilateral cross cousins exist only in societies in which $W^2 = I$ and can marry if and only if in addition $WC = CW$.

The condition $W^2 = I$ has a very simple interpretation: there must be an even number of clans in the society, and each clan must swap women as wives with another clan. The basic typology of societies will be

    I. *Bilateral marriage*, in which $W^2 = I$ and $WC = CW$.

    II. *Matrilateral marriage*, where $WC = CW$, but $W^2 \neq I$.

    III. *Patrilateral marriage*, where $WC = CW^{-1}$, but $W^2 \neq I$.

    IV. *Paired clans*, where $W^2 = I$, $WC \neq CW$.

    V. *Residual*.

In the first three names "cross cousin" is omitted since parallel first cousins can never marry. Only in I and IV societies can there exist bilateral cross cousins. Observe that any two of the three conditions imply the other: for example, if

$$WC = CW^{-1} \quad \text{and} \quad W^2 = I$$

then

$$W = W^{-1} \quad \text{and} \quad WC = CW.$$

2.6. Second-cousin Marriages

Second-cousin relationships are very much more complex than first-cousin relationships, and marriage for a particular type of second-cousin restricts the structure of the society much less. Yet in some of the more common kinds of societies satisfying Axioms 1–8 no first cousins may marry and the marriage prescription is formulated in terms of a whole set of types of second cousins. The groundwork is laid here for analyzing such societies. In addition it will be shown how the use of terms such as first cousin and second cousin tends to confound the analysis of societies satisfying Axioms 1–8, valuable though these terms are in helping us grow familiar with these systems.

There are sixteen kinds of second cousins logically possible where one is male and one female. In Fig. 2.5 a shorthand diagram is shown for each and a number assigned. By definition second cousins are grandchildren of two siblings (or equivalently great-grandchildren of a married couple). In the shorthand diagram is shown the sex of each sibling, each sibling's child, and each sibling's child's child. By convention the male is shown at the bottom left and his female second cousin at the bottom right.

Now think about each diagram in terms of clan membership. The two siblings at the top of a diagram are necessarily in the same clan (Axiom 4). In diagram 1 the two sons of the initial two brothers must also be in the same clan—although in general not in the common clan of their fathers—since they are the children of brothers (Axioms 2 and 4). Similarly the two daughters of the original two brothers in diagram 3 must be in the same clan. The children of two sisters also must be in the same clan—two sisters marry men from the same clan—so in diagram 2 the mother of male ego and the mother of his female second cousin are in the same clan. In all of the first eight diagrams the original two siblings are of the same sex; so in each of types 1–8 of second cousin the parent of male ego is in the same clan as the parent of his female second cousin.

Furthermore in each of diagrams 1–4 the parents of the second cousins are of the same sex; hence the second cousins themselves are in the same clan. Hence by exogamy (Axiom 6) second cousins of types 1, 2, 3, or 4 may never marry. On the other hand, in diagrams 5–8 the parents of second cousins are of opposite sex, though in the same clan as established above. As far as clan membership is concerned, then, second cousins of types 5–8 are in effect first cross cousins. That is, although their parents are not actually siblings, they are clan-siblings. Types 5 and 6 of second cousins are thus in clan terms matrilateral cross cousins, while types 7 and 8 are patrilateral cross cousins in clan terms; each pair can marry if and only if "true" or "blood" first cousins of that kind can marry.

To be objective about it, only in terms of familiar Western concepts is it appropriate to call types 1–8 second cousins. Earlier the classificatory system of kin roles was explained in detail. In this system the parent of the girl second cousin of type 5 or 6 is in fact called Mother's Brother.

Beneath each diagram in Fig. 2.5 is written the formula, in terms of C and W, for M_i, the permutation matrix which converts the clan of the male into the clan of his female second cousin of type i. Second cousins of type i may marry if and only if $M_i = W$. If the W and C algebra works, the same conclusions about clan membership and marriageability should be obtained by grinding the mathematical crank as were obtained above by direct reason-

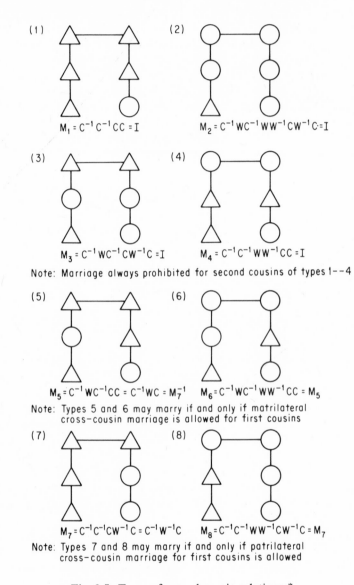

Fig. 2.5. Types of second-cousin relations.*

---

* M_i is the permutation matrix transforming the clan of male ego (lower left) to the clan of his female cousin (lower right) for type i. At each step of the tree the spouse who is not related to further members of the tree is omitted for visual clarity. C is the permutation matrix transforming father's clan into son's clan, and W the matrix transforming husband's

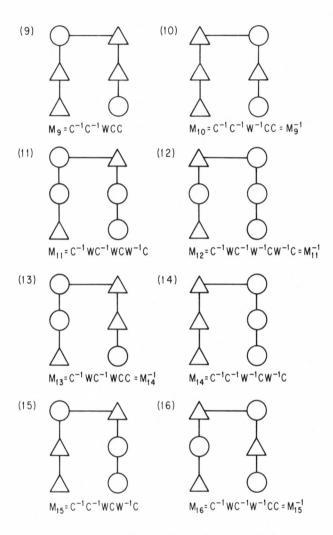

Fig. 2.5 (cont.). Types of second-cousin relations.

clan into wife's clan. I is the identity matrix: $I_{ii} = 1$; $I_{ij} = 0$, $i \neq j$. M^{-1} is the inverse of M: $M^{-1} M = M M^{-1} = I$. Male ego is allowed to marry his girl cousin of the ith type if and only if $M_i = W$.

ing. For type 1, $M_1 \equiv C^{-1} C^{-1} CC$, since no female appears among the parents and grandparents. Thus $M_1 = I$, the clan of male ego and his female second cousin is the same and they never may marry. In type 2 each step in the chain from male ego is female. To get from a mother's clan to her child's clan in terms of W and C operators requires first a transformation (W^{-1}) from mother's clan to her husband's clan before the transformation (C) to children's clan. Thus

$$M_2 \equiv (C^{-1}W)(C^{-1}W)(W^{-1}C)(W^{-1}C).$$

The associative law applies, so that the W and W^{-1} in the center may be multiplied, and $WW^{-1} = I$ by definition. Hence $M_2 = I$ after reduction. The same is true for M_3 and M_4.

For type 5 second cousins, $M_5 \equiv (C^{-1}W) C^{-1}CC$, by direct reading of the tree. $C^{-1}C = I$, so that $M_5 = C^{-1}WC$, as does M_6. Hence second cousins of types 5 and 6 marry if and only if

$$C^{-1}WC = W \quad \text{or} \quad WC = CW.$$

From the trees for types 7 and 8,

$$M_7 \equiv C^{-1} C^{-1}C (W^{-1}C)$$

and

$$M_8 \equiv C^{-1} (C^{-1}W)(W^{-1}C)(W^{-1}C),$$

whence after condensation it follows that types 7 and 8 marry if and only if $WC = CW^{-1}$, the same conditions as for "real" patrilateral cross cousins.

Hereafter "second cousins" of types 1–8 may be ignored. Both by direct reasoning and by algebraic derivations it has been shown that they are either siblings or first cross cousins in clan terms. That is, the natives will apply the classificatory kin term and the corresponding marriage rules for siblings (types 1–4) or first cross cousins (types 5–8) to them. Similarly, in native kinship terms a boy and a girl related as shown in the trees of Figs. 2.1 and 2.2 are not parallel first cousins but siblings, and are treated as such in the classificatory kin system of social structure.

Second cousins of types 9–16, however, are genuinely new kinds of kin in the classificatory kin system. The condition under which second cousins of one of these types can marry is quite complex. It would be a difficult task to derive all possible societies in which a given one of these types could be eligible spouses. In effect this task has been discussed earlier (Sec. 1.4) in connection with reductions of the general kin-role tree for a classificatory system (See Figs. 1.10 and 1.12.) It seems that only societies with sister exchange in marriage ($W^2 = I$) are found which make some of the types 9–16 of second cousins but not types 5–8 eligible spouses. The possibilities for such societies are analyzed in detail later. In effect then, types of second-cousin marriage are used only to provide a partial subclassification of Type IV societies, defined in the previous section.

One ambiguity remains. Societies have been classified above by whether a certain kind of cousin, in Western or "blood" terms, *may* marry. It was pointed out that in these terms a boy and a girl who are not cousins at all but stand in some other relation, say in a Type II (matrilateral first-cousin marriage) society, may perfectly well be eligible spouses. These societies, however, use classificatory kin terms in which all men in the same clan are brothers. In this terminology, discussed in detail earlier, the girl a boy marries in a Type II society *must* be Mother's Brother's Daughter to him, whatever other classificatory relationship she may also occupy with respect to him.

2.7. Bilateral Marriage Systems

Any element M of a group must have an order; i.e., a least positive integer f, such that $M^f = I$. Hereafter, let the order of W be q and the order of C be p: $W^q = I$, $2 \leq q \leq n$; $C^p = I$, $1 \leq p \leq n$. Here n is the number of elements in the group, or equivalently the number of clans in the society, as proved earlier. Note that $W \neq I$ by property 6.

Assume that $WC = CW$, and $W^2 = I$, or $q = 2$. Then $W^{-1}C = CW$ and $CW^{-1} = WC$. That is, consider societies in which either patrilateral or matrilateral cross cousins may marry, and thus societies in which pairs of clans exchange wives.

Case 1. Assume $W = C^j$, $1 \leq j < p$. Then $I = W^2 = C^{2j}$, and $2j \geq p$ by definition of p. But $C^{2j-p} = C^{2j}C^{-p} = IC^{-p} = (C^p)^{-1} = I$. If $2j > p$, then $2j - p > 0$; but also $2j < 2p$ so that $p > 2j - p > 0$, which contradicts the definition of p. Hence if $W = C^j$, p must be even and $2j = p$. Since all elements of the group are generated by W and C and since W is a power of C the group consists entirely of powers of C; i.e., it is the cyclic group. Moreover, the number of clans $n = p = 2j$.

Consider the case $j = 3$, $p = n = 6$. The multiplication table of the group is

$\cdot$	I	C	C^2	$C^3 = W$	C^4	C^5
$C^6 = I$	I	C	C^2	C^3	C^4	C^5
C	C	C^2	C^3	C^4	C^5	I
C^2	C^2	C^3	C^4	C^5	I	C
$W = C^3$	C^3	C^4	C^5	I	C	C^2
C^4	C^4	C^5	I	C	C^2	C^3
C^5	C^5	I	C	C^2	C^3	C^4

For example, the product of C^4 times C^3 is $C^7 = C^6C = C$, and this is entered in the row of C^4 in the column under C^3. Note that each element appears once and only once in each row and column.

The permutation matrices for C and W in the regular representation of this group are the two matrices which send the row of column headings into the row in the table opposite C and the row in the table opposite W respectively. Thus

$$
C = \begin{bmatrix}
0 & 0 & 0 & 0 & 0 & 1 \\
1 & 0 & 0 & 0 & 0 & 0 \\
0 & 1 & 0 & 0 & 0 & 0 \\
0 & 0 & 1 & 0 & 0 & 0 \\
0 & 0 & 0 & 1 & 0 & 0 \\
0 & 0 & 0 & 0 & 1 & 0
\end{bmatrix}, \quad
W = \begin{bmatrix}
0 & 0 & 0 & 1 & 0 & 0 \\
0 & 0 & 0 & 0 & 1 & 0 \\
0 & 0 & 0 & 0 & 0 & 1 \\
1 & 0 & 0 & 0 & 0 & 0 \\
0 & 1 & 0 & 0 & 0 & 0 \\
0 & 0 & 1 & 0 & 0 & 0
\end{bmatrix}.
$$

The validity of the regular representation was discussed in the Sec. 2.4 and is proved in the appendix. It is the only distinct representation of the given group by $n \times n$ permutation matrices which satisfies Axioms 1–8, as shown in the appendix. Other representations can be obtained by changing the order in which the group elements are written in the headings of the multiplication table, but this just amounts to a relabeling of the clans.

It is easier to interpret C and W when they are written in graphical form. Let the numerals 1, 2, . . ., 6 represent the clans. Let a solid arrow from numeral i to numeral j indicate that men in clan i marry women in clan j. Let a dotted arrow from numeral i to numeral k indicate that the children of a marriage contracted by a man in clan i are in clan k. In the society above let clan i be identified with ith row and column of each matrix. Then the diagram for the society is given by Fig. 6. We can present the diagram in many alternative forms. For example, Fig.7 represents the same society with the numerals placed differently. The general society which satisfies the conditions of Case 1 is represented by the obvious generalization of Fig. 6: a regular n-sided polyhedron in which dotted arrows connect the vertices in a single cycle around the perimeter, and in which each two vertices opposite each other

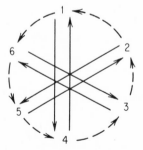

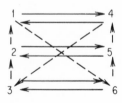

Figure 2.6   **Figure 2.7**

Six-clan bilateral marriage society with $W = C^3$. Solid arrow from 2 to 5 indicates that men in clan 2 marry women in clan 5, while the dotted arrow from 2 to 1 indicates that the children of men in clan 2 are in clan 1. The numbering of the clans is arbitrary.

Fig. 2.8. Two-clan bilateral marriage society, $W = C$.

(through the center) are connected by a pair of solid arrows. In the special case $W = C$ the diagram for the society is given by Fig. 8.

Case 2. The only alternative to Case 1 is $W \neq C^j$ for any $1 \leq j < p$; and then also $W \neq C^j$ for any $j > p$. Any element in the group generated by W and C can be written as WC^j or as C^j, $1 \leq j \leq p$, because $W^2 = I$ and W commutes with both C and its inverse. Thus there are at most $2p$ elements in the group.

Suppose two of these $2p$ elements are identical: there are three possibilities. (A) If $C^j = C^k$, $k \neq j$, we have a contradiction: let $k < j$, then $C^{j-k} = I$, and $j - k > 0$ but k and j by hypothesis are each $\leq p$; so $0 < j - k < p$, in contradiction to the definition of p as the order of C. (B) If $WC^j = WC^k$, $k \neq j$; we can cancel the W and this case reduces to (A). (C) If $WC^j = C^k$, $j \neq k$, then $W = C^{k-j}$, in contradiction to the basic stipulation for Case 2. Therefore there are exactly the $2p$ elements C^j and WC^j in the group; they are the set of n distinct matrices A_i in our earlier notation.

Case 2a. Suppose p is odd: then $p = 2r + 1$ for some integer $r \geq 0$. Consider the element (WC) from the list of $2p$ elements.

$$(WC)^{2r+1} = W^{2r+1}C^{2r+1} = W$$

since $W^2 = I$ and $2r + 1$ is the order of C. Similarly

$$(WC)^{2r+2} = W\, WC = C.$$

The group is generated by C and W, and since each is a power of (WC) all elements in the group are powers of (WC). In short the group is a cyclic group generated by the element (WC). The order of the generator must of course be $2p$, the number of elements in the group, and we see that

$$(WC)^{2(2r+1)} = [(WC)^{2r+1}]^2 = W^2 = I.$$

To simplify notation let us use the symbol G for (WC). There is no need to work out the correspondence between powers of G and our original list of elements WC^j and C^j. We note in passing that the order of $C = G^{2r+2}$ is the least integer multiple of $2r + 2$ which is also a multiple of $2(2r + 1)$.

The multiplication table for this group is identical with that for the group of Case 1, for the same number of clans, if C there is replaced by G; both are cyclic groups. The differences are

(i) The order of the group generated by G must be $2p$, twice an odd number, rather than any even number you like.

(ii) C is G^{p+1}.

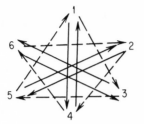

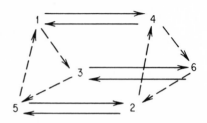

Fig. 2.9. Six-clan bilateral marriage society, $W = (WC)^3$, $C = (WC)^4$.

Fig. 2.10. Figure 2.9 drawn in three-dimensional perspective.

Consider the case $n = 2p = 6$, which is twice the odd number $p = 3$, as required. Then the matrix for W in the regular representation is the same as that shown for Case 1 since $W = G^3$. The matrix for C is for the permutation of the standard order of elements into the order in the row of the multiplication table for the fourth power of the generator: $G^4 = C$.

$$
C = \begin{bmatrix}
0 & 0 & 1 & 0 & 0 & 0 \\
0 & 0 & 0 & 1 & 0 & 0 \\
0 & 0 & 0 & 0 & 1 & 0 \\
0 & 0 & 0 & 0 & 0 & 1 \\
1 & 0 & 0 & 0 & 0 & 0 \\
0 & 1 & 0 & 0 & 0 & 0
\end{bmatrix}
$$

A diagram for this society parallel to that in Fig. 6 for the six-clan group of Case 1 is shown in Fig. 9. It is easier to interpret the diagram if it is visualized in three dimensions as in the perspective diagram of Fig. 10. In the special case of two clans, $n = 2p = 2$; so $p = 1$, or $W = G$ and $C = G^2 = I$. The diagram for this case is given in Fig. 2.11, which is parallel to Fig. 9.

The next largest society for Case 2a beyond those in Figs. 11 and 10 is for $n = 10$ or $p = 5$. The diagram will be like Fig. 10 only with pentagons instead of triangles as the end pieces. What about societies with a diagram like that in Fig. 10 except that the end polygons are squares, not triangles? They fall under Case 2b.

Case 2b. Suppose p, the order of C, is even. $W \neq C^j$ for any j: so no power of C can generate all the $2p$ elements in the group. Suppose some power j of (WC^k), $1 \leq k \leq p$, is C: that is

$$(WC^k)^j = C.$$

Fig. 2.11. Two-clan bilateral marriage society, $C = I$.

Certainly j cannot be odd since then $W = C^{1-jk}$. Let j be even: $j = 2j'$, and $C = (WC^k)^j = W^{2j'}C^{2kj'} = C^{2(kj')}$. Then $C^{2(kj')-1} = I$. But the only powers of C which yield the identity are p and integer multiples of p. Now p is even, whereas $2(kj') - 1$ is odd, and no odd number is an integer multiple of an even number. This is a contradiction; so it must be that no power of any element WC^k can equal C. Thus neither any element WC^j nor any element C^j can generate the whole group of $2p$ elements: C^j and WC^j, $1 \leq j \leq p$. We have a new kind of group; it can be shown that it is the "direct product" of two cyclic groups, and this new group is usually symbolized as $S_{q \times p}$, where here $q = 2$, the order of W.

The multiplication table for the case $p = 4$ we can find by direct calculation:

.	I	C	C^2	C^3		W	WC	WC^2	WC^3
I	I	C	C^2	C^3		W	WC	WC^2	WC^3
C	C	C^2	C^3	I		WC	WC^2	WC^3	W
C^2	C^2	C^3	I	C		WC^2	WC^3	W	WC
C^3	C^3	I	C	C^2		WC^3	W	WC	WC^2
W	W	WC	WC^2	WC^3		I	C	C^2	C^3
WC	WC	WC^2	WC^3	W		C	C^2	C^3	I
WC^2	WC^2	WC^3	W	WC		C^2	C^3	I	C
WC^3	WC^3	W	WC	WC^2		C^3	I	C	C^2

The dotted lines mark off the four natural blocs in the table; note the upper left bloc is identical with the lower right bloc, and the upper right bloc with the lower left bloc. Within each of the blocs the pattern of entries is the same as or parallel to the arrangement in the multiplication table for the cyclic group of order 4. We really need only the two rows in the table for C and W in order to find the permutation matrices which represent them. If we express these matrices in the same graphical convention as before, the diagram for the society with $p = 4$ is given in Fig. 12, which is drawn in three-dimensional perspective.

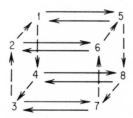

Fig. 2.12. Eight-clan bilateral marriage society, $C^4 = I$: the abstract group generated by C and W is not cyclic.

It should be clear without formal proof how to generalize to any number of clans the multiplication tables and diagrams both for the six-clan society of Fig. 9 and for the eight-clan society of Fig. 12. One limitation of the diagrams should now be evident: a superficial comparison of Figs. 10 and 12 yields no hint that the abstract groups for the two societies are of quite different kinds. In fact the multiplication tables for the two societies can be rewritten so as to have similar forms.

Figure 1.6 in the previous chapter is the reduced role tree for all bilateral marriage systems.

2.8. Matrilateral Marriage Systems

Assume that $WC = CW$, but $W^2 \neq I$ so that $WC \neq CW^{-1}$ and $CW \neq W^{-1}C$. As before, let q be the order of W and p the order of C. Thus $C^p = I$, and $W^q = I, q > 2$.

Case 1. Assume $W = C^j$, where j is the smallest positive integer for which the equation holds. Then $1 \leq j < p; p > 1$; and also $j \neq p/2$, or else bilateral cross-cousin marriage would be allowed. C generates W and thus all elements in the cyclic group of the society, which must have p clans.

We prove that each distinct value of j gives a distinct society. In Sec. 2.6 we gave the definition: *Two societies are distinct if and only if there is at least one kind of female relation of a man who can marry him in one society but not in the other.*

Let $M = C^k W^l$ be the relation matrix or element for an arbitrary relation of a man to a woman. $M = C^{k+lj}$ by hypothesis. The condition for marriage is $W = M$. The necessary and sufficient condition for marriage is thus

$$k + lj = sp + j,$$

where s is some integer, since the group is cyclic of order p. This kind of equation is often written

$$k + (l - 1)j \equiv 0 \qquad (\text{mod } p);$$

i.e., $k + lj$ is congruent to j, modulo p.

Suppose $M = W$ for a society with one value j if and only if $M' = W'$ for another society with $W' = (C')^{j'}$; both societies have p clans, or $C^p = (C')^p = I$. Then

$$k + (l - 1)j = sp,$$

$$k + (l - 1)j' = s'p,$$

s' some integer, are either both true or both false. To be definite, let $j \geq j'$. Consider the relation for $l = 0, k = j$. The first equation is then $0 = sp$, which is certainly valid. The second equation becomes

$$j - j' = s'p.$$

Now $p > j - j' \geq 0$, so s' must be zero and $j = j'$, which concludes the proof.

This proof was given in a framework more general than was needed in order to indicate how to investigate the number of distinct societies if the definition of distinctness is relaxed. If, for example, only marriages of men and women in the same generation (with respect to some reference ancestor) are of interest, many societies distinct by the definition above will no longer be distinct.

The procedure for establishing the representations of C and W is the same as in Case 1 of bilateral marriage, since the group in each case is the cyclic group generated by C. These matrilateral marriage societies can have any number of clans, however. The diagram representing C and W for a matrilateral marriage society with $W = C^j$ is an obvious generalization of Fig. 6. Figures 13 (a) and (b) are the diagrams for $j = 2$ and 3 respectively and $p = 5$. Societies (a) and (b) are distinct because the direction of the interior solid arrows in (a) parallels the direction of the cycle of dotted arrows in (a), but not in (b).

Case 2. Assume $W \neq C^j$ but $W^2 = C^m$, where $1 \leq m < p$, since $m = p$ corresponds to bilateral marriage, and $p > 1$ for the same reason. The analysis is parallel to that for Case 2 of bilateral marriage. All elements can be written as WC^k or C^k, and all of the latter $2p$ elements are distinct. The multiplication table is specified by

$$(WC^k)(WC^{k'}) = C^{k+k'+m}.$$

Consider the simplest case: $p = 2$. Then $m = 1$, i.e., $W^2 = C$. The four distinct elements are $C, I = C^2, W, WC$, and the multiplication table is

$\cdot$	I	C	W	WC
I	I	C	W	WC
C	C	I	WC	W
W	W	WC	C	I
WC	WC	W	I	C

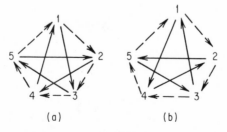

(a) (b)

Fig. 2.13. (a) Five-clan matrilateral marriage society, $W = C^2$. (b) Same as (a), except $W = C^3$.

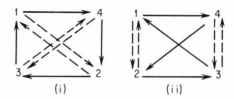

Fig. 2.14. The four-clan matrilateral marriage society, $W^2 = C$: (i) is the simplest way to draw the diagram but (ii) generalizes more easily. $W \neq C^j$, $C^2 = I$.

We see by inspection that this is actually a cyclic group generated by the element W or equally well by WC: see Fig. 14.

There exists one society for each value of m, since we can exhibit the multiplication table of its group. There exists only one such society for a given m since C and W are explicitly indicated in the list of elements and the multiplication rule is uniquely fixed by m. It is obvious that if two societies have different values of p, the order of C, they must be different regardless of m since the number of clans will be different. It is equally clear from the way we have defined Case 2 that there is no overlap with Case 1 or with the bilateral marriage cases.

It remains to be shown that different values of m for a given p lead to distinct societies (see the definition of distinctness given for Case 1). Let $M = W^i C^j$ be the general relation operator. If i is even, $M = C^{j - im/2}$, which can never be W for Case 2. Therefore i can be written as $2i' + 1$ if marriage is allowed for a given relation, and the condition for marriage is

$$W = M = W^{2i' + 1} C^j = WC^{i'm + j} \quad \text{or} \quad i'm + j \equiv 0 \pmod p.$$

Arbitrarily set $i' = 1$, and choose $j = -m$, so that marriage is allowed. Assume that another society, for which $(W')^2 = (C')^{m'}$, is not distinct from the first. Then when $i' = 1$ and $j = -m$

$$i'm' + j \equiv 0 \pmod p;$$

i.e.,

$$m' - m \equiv 0 \pmod p.$$

Without loss of generality we can assume $m' > m$, and since each is less than p the only solution to the modular equation is $m' = m$. This completes the proof.

Multiplication by C merely permutes the elements C^k among themselves and the elements WC^k among themselves. In the diagram for any matrilateral society with $W^2 = C^m$, $W \neq C^j$ it is therefore clear that the dotted arrows will connect p clans in one cycle and the other p clans in a second cycle, regardless of m, $1 \leq m < p$. On the other hand multiplication by W sends C^k into WC^k and WC^k into C^{k+m}. The solid arrows, representing the effect of W, must therefore each connect a vertex in one regular p-sided polygon to some

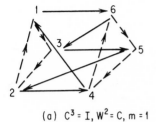

Identical with (a) except
that direction of dotted
arrows in the two
triangles is reversed

(a) $C^3 = I, W^2 = C, m = 1$ (b) $C^3 = I, W^2 = C^2, m = 2$

Fig. 2.15. The six-clan matrilateral marriage societies
with $W \neq C^j$, and $W^2 = C^m$. Drawn in three-dimensional perspective. Note that the W arrows (solid) form
a single cycle of six links.

vertex in the other polygon. In fact, if the polygons are lined up parallel to
each other in three dimensions in the most convenient way, each of the solid
arrows beginning from a vertex of the left-hand polygon will go straight to
the corresponding vertex of the right-hand polygon. Figures 15 and 16 give
further examples of such diagrams.

The General Case. It should now be clear how the general case is developed
in our breakdown of matrilateral marriage societies. Suppose $W^a \neq C^b$ for
any $1 \leq a < c$, no matter what b is, $1 \leq b < p$. Then assume $W^c = C^m$
for $1 \leq m \leq p$. (Only in Case 2, where $c = 2$, is $m = p$ excluded, so as to
rule out bilateral marriage.) It can be proved in a manner analogous to
that for Cases 1 and 2 that there is exactly one distinct society for given p, c
and m. The list of distinct elements can be written in c ordered classes: C^k,
WC^k, W^2C^k, . . . , $W^{c-1}C^k$, where $1 \leq k \leq p$, whatever m is. The multiplication table is defined by $W^c = C^m$. Multiplication by C simply permutes
the elements in a given class. Multiplication by W simply transforms an
element in one class to the corresponding element in the next higher class;
except that $W(W^{c-1}C^k) = C^{k+m}$—that is, W transforms each element in the
highest class into some element in the lowest class.

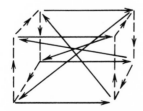

Fig. 2.16. An eight-clan matrilateral marriage society
with $W \neq C^j$, $C^4 = I$, $W^2 = C^2$. Note that the W
arrows (solid) form two cycles of 4 clans each.

The nature of the diagram for a society with c and m fixed should now be clear. The diagram can be drawn in three dimensions, with c regular p-sided polygons drawn parallel to each other. The successive vertices of each polygon are connected in a clockwise cycle by dotted arrows, and from each vertex there is a solid arrow to the corresponding vertex of the next polygon to the right. Then from each vertex of the cth polygon there is a solid arrow to some vertex of the first polygon, the exact vertex depending on the choice of m, which affects the diagram only in this last respect. Figure 17 is a schematic example for a society with $c > 2$, $p = 4$, and m unspecified.

The reader should check for himself that male ego is always allowed to marry his mother's brother's daughter in Fig. 17. In the special case $m = p$ the solid arrows form p closed loops, each of c clans, since then $c = q$. If $p = 4$ and $m = 2$ the solid arrows form two closed loops, each of $2c$ clans. If $p = 4$ and $m = 1$ or 3 the solid arrows form a single closed loop containing all $4c$ clans, i.e., W is the generator of the group of the society, which must be cyclic.

Summary. Matrilateral societies have been classified according to the lowest power of W, namely c, which equals any power of C, call the power C^m. Except for Cases 1 and 2, there are exactly p distinct societies for each value of c, where $C^p = I$. All of these societies contain c rings of p clans each; the men of one clan have children in the next clan of the ring, and obtain their wives from the corresponding clan in the next ring. The order q of W depends not so much on c as on the values of m and p. The order of W is always a multiple of c. When p is odd and $m \neq p$ the order of W, $q = cp$; i.e., all relation matricies in the society are powers of W. When $m = p$ the order of W, $q = c$, whatever p is. When p is even the possibilities are numerous. Figure 1.5 in the previous chapter is the reduced role tree for all matrilateral marriage systems.

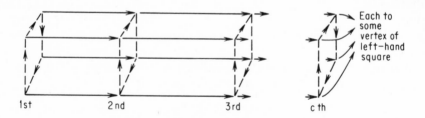

Fig. 2.17. The general case of a matrilateral marriage society when $C^4 = I$, $W^a \neq C^b$ for any b and $a < c$; and $W^c = C^m$, c and m unspecified.

2.9. Patrilateral Marriage Systems

Assume $WC = CW^{-1}$ and equivalently $CW = W^{-1}C$, but $WC \neq CW$ and thus $W^2 \neq 1$. It follows that

$$WC^{2j} = C^{2j} W \quad \text{and} \quad WC^{2j+1} = C^{2j+1} W^{-1},$$

or more generally

$$W^k C^{2j} = C^{2j} W^k$$

whereas

$$W^k C^{2j+1} = C^{2j+1} W^{-k}.$$

$W \neq C^j$ for any j since W and C do not commute, and similarly $C \neq W^k$ for any k. Neither C nor W can generate the group of elements for a patrilateral marriage society, although this does not mean the group cannot be cyclic.

Case 1. Assume $W^2 = C^l$, $1 \leq l < p$. Consider the product $W(WC^{p-l}) = W^2 C^{p-l} = C^p = I$. Hence $W^{-1} = WC^{p-l}$. Let $p - l$ be odd; then

$$(WC^{p-l}) W = (C^{p-l} W^{-1}) W = C^{p-l} \neq I,$$

but yet $(WC^{p-l}) W = W^{-1} W = I$, which is a contradiction.

Therefore, $p - l$ is even, and $W^{-1} = WC^{p-l}$. Further,

$$C^{2j+1} W = W^{-1} C^{2j+1} = WC^{2j+1+p-l} = C^{2j+1+p-l} W^{-1},$$

or

$$C^{2j+1} W = C^{2j+1+p-l} WC^{p-l} = C^{2j+1+2(p-l)} W$$

Hence $C^{2(p-l)} = I$. But $l < p$; so $p - l < p$, or $2(p - l) < 2p$. It follows that $2(p - l) = p$, or $p = 2l$. Thus

$$W^{-1} = WC^{p-l} = WC^l.$$

Yet by definition of l, $C^l = W^2$. Hence

$$W^{-1} = WC^l = W^3 \quad \text{or} \quad W^4 = I$$

To summarize, if $W^2 = C^l$, $q = 4$ or $W^4 = I$, whereas $p = 2l$ or $C^{2l} = I$. Furthermore l must be an even number, since $p = 2l$, and $p - l$ is even. In short, if $W^2 = C^l$, $l = 2l'$; the order of W, $q = 4$, so that $W^4 = I$; while $p = 4l' = 2l$. There is exactly one society for each even value of l, and none for each odd value.

All relation matrices for the society can be written as C^j or as WC^j, $1 \leq j \leq 4 l' = p$. No two of these elements can be equal; for example, if

$$C^j = WC^k$$

then

$$W = C^{j-k}$$

so that W and C commute. There are $8l' = 2p$ elements and thus clans. To complete the derivation we must list the rules of multiplication:

(i) $(C^j)(C^k) = C^{j+k}$

(ii) $(WC^j)(C^k) = WC^{j+k}$

(iii) $(C^{2k'+1})(WC^j) = W^{-1}C^{j+2k'+1} = WC^{j+2k'+1+l}$

(iv) $(C^{2k'})(WC^j) = WC^{j+2k'}$

(v) $(WC^{2k'})(WC^j) = C^{j+2k'+l}$

(vi) $(WC^{2k'+1})(WC^j) = C^{j+2k'+1}$

where rules (iii)–(vi) are differentiated by whether the power of C in the first element of the product is even or odd.

Consider the simplest case: $l = 2$, a society with eight clans. The multiplication table is

•	I	C	C^2	C^3	W	WC	WC^2	WC^3
I	I	C	C^2	C^3	W	WC	WC^2	WC^3
C	C	C^2	C^3	I	WC^3	W	WC	WC^2
C^2	C^2	C^3	I	C	WC^2	WC^3	W	WC
C^3	C^3	I	C	C^2	WC	WC^2	WC^3	W
W	W	WC	WC^2	WC^3	C^2	C^3	I	C
WC	WC	WC^2	WC^3	W	C	C^2	C^3	I
WC^2	WC^2	WC^3	W	WC	I	C	C^2	C^3
WC^3	WC^3	W	WC	WC^2	C^3	I	C	C^2

The diagram representing the W and C matrices for this society with $l = 2$ is shown in Fig. 18 in two arrangements. Observe that the first is exactly like Fig. 16 for one kind of matrilateral marriage society, except that the two dotted cycles run in opposite directions in Fig. 18(i). The generalization of Fig. 18(i) to any l should be obvious. The next largest society will have 16 clans and the dotted cycles will be octagons.

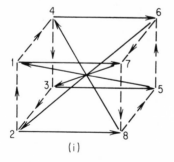 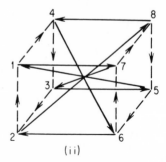

Fig. 2.18. The eight-clan society with patrilateral marriage, in two equivalent arrangements. $W^2 = C^2$ (i.e., $l = 2$), $W^4 = I$, $p = 4$.

Case 2. Suppose $W^2 \neq C^l$ and $W^3 = C^m$, $1 \leq m \leq p$. Consider $W(W^2 C^{p-m}) = W^3 C^{p-m} = C^p = I$. Then $W^2 C^{p-m} = W^{-1}$. Next consider, for $p - m$ odd, $(W^2 C^{p-m}) W = W^2 W^{-1} C^{p-m} = W C^{p-m}$. Now $W C^{p-m} \neq I$ or else the group would be cyclic and W would commute with C. This is a contradiction; so $p - m$ is even and $W^{-1} = W^2 C^{p-m}$.

Suppose $q = 3q' + 1$. Then $I = W^q = (W^3)^{q'} W = C^{q'm} W$; or $W = C^{-q'm}$, which is a contradiction. A similar contradiction follows from $q = 3q' + 2$. Thus q, the order of W, must be a multiple of 3. Furthermore, $I = W^q = W^{3q'} = C^{mq'}$ so that mq' is an integer multiple of p. Also $I = (C^p)^m = (C^m)^p = W^{3p}$, so that $3p$ is an integer multiple of q, or p is an integer multiple of q'.

Consider

$$C^{2j+1} W = W^{-1} C^{2j+1} = W^2 C^{2j+1+p-m} = C^{2j+1+p-m} W^{-2};$$

or

$$C^{2j+1} W = C^{2j+1+p-m} W^2 C^{p-m} W^2 C^{p-m};$$

or

$$C^{2j+1} W = C^{2j+1+3(p-m)} W^3 W = C^{2j+1+2(p-m)+p} W.$$

Thus $I = C^{2(p-m)+p}$.

Next consider

$$C^{2j+1} W^2 = W^{-1} C^{2j+1} W = W^2 C^{2j+1+p-m} W$$

$$= C^{2j+1+p-m} W^{-1} = C^{2j+1+p-m} W^2 C^{p-m}$$

$$= C^{2j+1+2(p-m)} W^2$$

Hence $I = C^{2(p-m)}$.

But $C^p = I$; so these two derivations both lead to $C^{2(p-m)} = I$ or $2(p - m) = tp$ where t is some integer. But $1 \leq m \leq p$. So either $m = p$; or else $2(p - m) = p$; i.e., $p = 2m$. Thus $p - m = 0$; or else $p - m = m$, and therefore m can only be even.

Again consider $W^{-1} = W^2 C^{p-m}$. Either $m = p$ and $W^{-1} = W^2$ or $W^3 = I$; or $p = 2m$ and $W^{-1} = W^2 C^m = W^5$; so $W^6 = I$. This confirms but makes much more definite our earlier findings that q must be a multiple of 3, and that p is a multiple of q'.

The list of all distinct elements in the group can be written as C^k, $W C^k$, and $W^2 C^k$. The list is exhaustive, since, for example,

$$C^{2j+1} W^2 = W^{-2} C^{2j+1} = W^4 C^{2j+1+2(p-m)},$$

or

$$C^{2j+1} W^2 = W C^{2j+1+2p-m}.$$

No two elements in this list are equal, since, for example, if $W C^k = W^2 C^{k'}$ then

$$W = C^{k-k'}$$

and the group is cyclic. Therefore there are $3p$ elements and $3p$ clans in each of the two societies for which $W^3 = C^m$, $W^2 \neq C^l$.

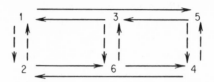

Fig. 2.19. The smallest society with patrilateral marriage. $W^3 = I$, $C^2 = I$, (i.e., $p = m$).

It is straightforward though tedious to work out the multiplication rules that summarize the multiplication table for a given society when the list of distinct elements is chosen as above.

Case 2a. Let $m = p$ so that $W^3 = I$ and $W^{-1} = W^2$. There apparently is no restriction on the value of p except $p > 1$.

Take the simplest case, $p = 2$. Then there are six clans and the standard list of elements is C, I, WC, W, W^2C, W^2. The multiplication table is found to be after some calculation

$\cdot$	I	C	W	WC	W^2	W^2C
I	I	C	W	WC	W^2	W^2C
C	C	I	W^2C	W^2	WC	W
W	W	WC	W^2	W^2C	I	C
WC	WC	W	C	I	W^2C	W^2
W^2	W^2	W^2C	I	C	W	WC
W^2C	W^2C	W^2	WC	W	C	I

The diagram for this, the smallest society with patrilateral marriage, is given in Fig. 19.

The generalization of the $m = p$ case to larger p is not as obvious as it has been in all previous cases. For example, the relevant two rows of the multiplication table for $p = m = 3$ are

$\cdot$	I	C	C^2	W	WC	WC^2	W^2	W^2C	W^2C^2
C	C	C^2	I	W^2C	W^2C^2	W^2	WC	WC^2	W
W	W	WC	WC^2	W^2	W^2C	W^2C^2	I	C	C^2

and the diagram for the society is given in Fig. 20.

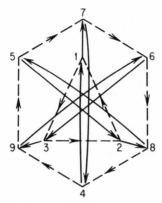

Fig. 2.20. Nine-clan patrilateral marriage society with $W^3 = I$, $C^3 = I$, $W^3 = C^3$ (i.e., $m = p = 3$). It does not satisfy the uniformity assumption, Property 8.

This nine-clan society would seem to be an important example because it is the first society of all those considered so far in which the clans are not divided into cycles with the same number of members. It is clear that this departure from equal cycles of dotted arrows can only occur for odd p. For example, when $p = 4 = m$, the diagram for the society can be shown to be that in Fig. 21.

On closer inspection we see that Fig. 20 violates an axiom—namely Axiom 8 —for our societies. Great-grandsons, in the male line, of clan 1 men are also in clan 1, but this is not true of clan 9 men. Let us examine the matrix representation of C:

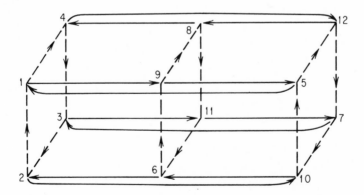

Fig. 2.21. Twelve-clan patrilateral marriage society with $W^3 = I$, $C^4 = I$, $W^3 = C^4$ (i.e., $m = p = 4$).

	I	C	C^2	W	WC	WC^2	W^2	W^2C	W^2C^2
I	0	0	1	0	0	0	0	0	0
C	1	0	0	0	0	0	0	0	0
C^2	0	1	0	0	0	0	0	0	0
W	0	0	0	0	0	0	0	0	1
WC	0	0	0	0	0	0	1	0	0
WC^2	0	0	0	0	0	0	0	1	0
W^2	0	0	0	0	0	1	0	0	0
W^2C	0	0	0	1	0	0	0	0	0
W^2C^2	0	0	0	0	1	0	0	0	0

To simplify notation let

$$P = \begin{bmatrix} 0 & 0 & 1 \\ 1 & 0 & 0 \\ 0 & 1 & 0 \end{bmatrix}.$$

Then we can write C in terms of P:

$$C = \begin{bmatrix} P & 0 & 0 \\ 0 & 0 & P \\ 0 & P & 0 \end{bmatrix}.$$

Then we find

$$C^2 = \begin{bmatrix} P^2 & 0 & 0 \\ 0 & P^2 & 0 \\ 0 & 0 & P^2 \end{bmatrix} \quad \text{and} \quad \begin{bmatrix} P^3 & 0 & 0 \\ 0 & 0 & P^3 \\ 0 & P^3 & 0 \end{bmatrix} = C^3 \neq I.$$

Thus there is a contradiction in assuming $m = p = 3$.

Let us retrace our steps to the very beginning of our considerations of patrilateral marriage, where we showed

$$WC^{2j+1} = C^{2j+1}W^{-1}.$$

Now suppose p is odd; i.e., $p = 2p' + 1$. Then

$$WC^{2p'+1} = C^{2p'+1}W^{-1},$$

but

$$C^{2p'+1} = I;$$

so

$$W = W^{-1} \quad \text{or} \quad W^2 = I,$$

contradicting the stipulated condition. Hence for any case of patrilateral marriage we know the order of C must be even, or $p = 2p'$, even before we consider special kinds of patrilateral marriage. We did not have to face this requirement in Case 1, for there p had to be even for other reasons.

We can also notice a more general point about diagrams of societies.

Regardless of the kinds of marriages allowed, in the diagram for any society satisfying our axioms the dotted arrows must occur only in cycles of the same length, and similarly for the solid arrows. Otherwise Axiom 8 is violated. We have proved in the preliminary sections of this chapter that the mathematical machinery we have set up automatically guarantees this and other aspects of Axiom 8. But Fig. 20 gives us an example of how easy it is to apply the machinery mistakenly.

Case 2b. Now we consider the other kind of patrilateral marriage society for $W^3 = C^m$; namely that for $p = 2m$, m even. Then $W^6 = I$, and $W^{-1} = W^5$.

The smallest m is 2; so the smallest p is 4 and the minimum number of elements or clans is 12. For this case the relevant two lines of the group multiplication table are found to be

$\cdot$	I	C	C^2	C^3	W	WC	WC^2	WC^3	W^2	W^2C	W^2C^2	W^2C^3
C	C	C^2	C^3	I	W^2C^3	W^2	W^2C	W^2C^2	WC^3	W	WC	WC^2
W	W	WC	WC^2	WC^3	W^2	W^2C	W^2C^2	W^2C^3	C^2	C^3	I	C

The diagram is exhibited in Fig. 22 in two equivalent forms. Considerable experimentation is necessary to find the form which is visually simplest. The three-dimensional perspective drawing shown in Fig. 22(ii) seems clearer than any two-dimensional diagram even in this more complex case. Note that Fig. 22 is the companion of Fig. 21; there are three twelve-clan patrilateral marriage societies, the third being a generalization of Fig. 19. Especially when the diagram is complex, the reader should check it visually: e.g., confirm for yourself that a man in clan 5 in Fig. 22 (or Fig. 21) can marry his father's sister's daughter but not his mother's brother's daughter. It is also helpful to the reader to confirm visually that there is a female relation whom male ego can marry in Fig. 21 but not in Fig. 22 (e.g., male ego's ZHZHZ).

The general case. In connection with Fig. 20 we proved that the order p of C must always be even. Moreover, if the minimum power of W which equals some power of C is z, then it is easy to show in the same way as for Cases 1 and 2 that there are zp clans in the society. For given p and z there will be two societies, one for which $W^z = C^p = I$ and the other for which $W^z = C^{p/2}$. In the former case the order q of W is just z, whereas in the latter case $q = 2z$. (In the special case $z = 2$, the $W^z = C^p$ society has bilateral marriage and so must be excluded.) There is a further restriction on the second type of society, in which $W^z = C^{p/2}$: $p/2$ must be even so that p must be a multiple of 4. In Table 2.1 the allowed combinations of z and p values are shown for both types of patrilateral society, together with the corres-

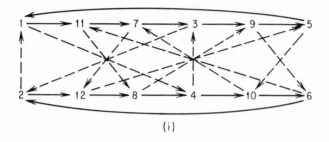

(i)

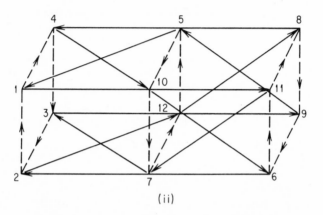

(ii)

Fig. 2.22. Two equivalent forms of a 12-clan patrilateral marriage society, $p = 4$, $W^3 = C^2$ (i.e., $m = 2$), and $W^6 = I$.

ponding numbers of clans and the order of W. Figure 1.7 of the previous chapter is the reduced role tree for all patrilateral marriage systems.

The proof for this general case of patrilateral marriage is as follows: $C^p = I$, p is order of C, and suppose $W^z = C^j$, with no lower power of W equal to any power of C. Necessarily $1 \leq j \leq p$. The fundamental lemmas for patrilateral marriage are, for general j,

$$WC^{2j+1} = C^{2j+1}W^{-1}, \qquad WC^{2j} = C^{2j}W.$$

If p were odd, the first lemma would lead to a contradiction.

Consider the following product:

$$W[W^{z-1}C^{p-j}] = C^p = I.$$

Thus it must be that

$$W^{-1} = W^{z-1}C^{p-j}.$$

But from considering the reverse product, we also have $W^{-1} = W^z C^{p-j} W^{-1}$, which if $p - j$ is odd becomes $W^{-1} = W^{z+1}C^{p-j}$. But $W^2 \neq I$. Therefore $p - j$ is even; therefore j is even.

Now for the basic step. Consider

$$WC^{2k+1} = C^{2k+1} W^{-1} = C^{2k+1} W^{z-1} C^{p-j}$$
$$= (W^{-1})^{z-1} C^{2k+1+p-j}$$
$$= [W^{z-1} C^{p-j}]^{z-1} C^{2k+1+p-j}$$
$$= W^{zz-2z+1} C^{2k+1+z(p-j)}$$
$$= W(C^j)^{z-2} C^{2k+1+z(p-j)}$$
$$= WC^{2k+1+zp-2j} = WC^{2k+1} C^{-2j},$$

Hence

$$I = C^{-2j} \quad \text{or} \quad C^{2j} = I.$$

Now by hypothesis $1 \leq j \leq p$; so either $2j = p$; or $2j = 2p$, $j = p$. Hence $W^z = C^{p/2}$, or $W^z = C^p = I$ are the only two possibilities.

$W^z = I$	$W^z = C^{p/2}$	z	q	p	Number of clans $= zp$
		1		forbidden	
	√	2	4	4, 8, 12, $\cdots$, $4j$, $\cdots$	8, 16, 24, $\cdots$, $8j$, $\cdots$
√		3	3	2, 4, 6, 8, $\cdots$, $2j$, $\cdots$	6, 12, 18, 24, $\cdots$, $6j$, $\cdots$
	√	3	6	4, 8, 12, $\cdots$, $4j$, $\cdots$	12, 24, 36, $\cdots$, $12j$, $\cdots$
√		4	4	2, 4, 6, 8, $\cdots$, $2j$, $\cdots$	8, 16, 24, $\cdots$, $8j$, $\cdots$
	√	4	8	4, 8, 12, $\cdots$, $4j$, $\cdots$	16, 32, 48, $\cdots$, $16j$, $\cdots$
√		N	N	2, 4, 6, 8, $\cdots$, $2j$, $\cdots$	$2N$, $4N$, $6N$, $\cdots$, $2jN$, $\cdots$
	√	N	$2N$	4, 8, 12, $\cdots$, $4j$, $\cdots$	$4N$, $8N$, $12N$, $\cdots$, $4jN$, $\cdots$

Table 2.1. Table of properties of the generators C and W for all distinct patrilateral marriage societies. For each value of q (the order of W) the allowed values of p (the order of C) are listed in that row. In the right column of each row are given the number of clans in the society with a value of p given in the corresponding position in the previous column in the same row. The basic parameter z is the minimum power of W which equals any power of C: as shown in the first two columns, either $W^z = C^p = I$, or $W^z = C^{p/2}$.

It is a straightforward though tedious matter to derive the multiplication table for any particular society in Table 2.1. Figures 19 and 21 are so simple that one can easily see what the diagram is for any society with $W^z = I$: there are z cycles of dotted arrows each with p links, and corresponding points in these cycles are connected by a closed loop of solid arrows. The diagrams for societies with $W^z = C^{p/2}$ are not as easy to describe: see Figs. 18 and 22.

However, a third way of drawing the twelve-clan society of Fig. 22, a way parallel to that in Fig. 18(ii) for the eight-clan society, reveals clearly the basic structure of societies with $W^z = C^{p/2}$ and in particular explains visually

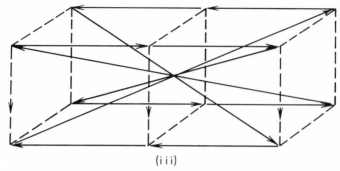

(iii)

Fig. 2.22(iii). A third diagram of the 12-clan patrilateral society in which $p = 4$, $z = 3$, and $W^z = C^{p/2}$. This is parallel to Fig. 2.18(ii), and any society with $W^z = C^{p/2}$ can be drawn in a form parallel to these two figures.

why p must be a multiple of 4. In Fig. 22 (iii) the direction of each cycle of dotted arrows is the same, clockwise as viewed from the right. A chain of solid arrows starting from a vertex of the left dotted cycle returns to the opposite vertex in the left dotted cycle. Therefore, if p is not a multiple of 4, there will be two solid arrows entering that opposite vertex, since in all patrilateral diagrams the direction of the chain of solid arrows starting from a given vertex of a dotted cycle is opposite to the direction of its neighbor chains starting from the two adjacent vertices. The easiest way to see why p cannot be an odd multiple of 2 is to try to draw the diagram parallel to Fig. 18(ii) for hexagons rather than squares. As a final exercise to test his understanding of these models, the reader should prove why the diagram in Fig. 23 is not an allowed patrilateral society. Certainly each male ego in this society, whatever his clan, can marry his Father's Sister's Daughter (FZD). [*Hint:* Axiom 8 is violated.]

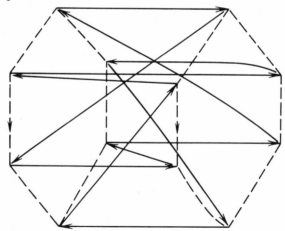

Fig. 2.23. Why is this not an allowed society with patrilateral marriage?

2.10. Paired-clan Marriage Systems

There are many prescribed systems satisfying the eight axioms in which first cousins of no kind may marry. An interesting special case is that in which wives are exchanged between pairs of clans (as is also true in bilateral first-cousin marriage). Assume $WC \neq CW$, and $W = W^{-1}$: this will be the definition of societies with paired-clan marriage, earlier called Type IV societies.

Any minimum list of distinct elements in the group of such a society must include I, W, C, WC, and CW. There must be a sixth element, too, which we can take to be WCW. We prove this by showing that no element can equal any element in the list before it: $W = I$ is excluded by Axiom 6. $C = I$ or W implies that C and W commute. If $WC = C$, $W = I$; if $WC = W$, $C = I$; if $WC = I$, then $W = C^{-1}$ so that W and C commute. $CW \neq C$, W, or I for parallel reasons. $CW \neq WC$ by stipulation. If $WCW = CW$, $W = I$; if $WCW = C$, $CW = W^{-1}C = WC$; if $WCW = W$, $CW = I$; if $WCW = I$, $CW = W^{-1} = W$; if $WCW = WC$, $W = I$.

The inverse of C must be specified as one of the other five elements if the above list is to be the entire set of elements in a group. C^{-1} cannot be W as shown above. If C^{-1} is I, C is I. If $C^{-1} = WC$ or $C^{-1} = CW$ then $C^2 = W^{-1} = W$, so that $WC = C^3 = CW$. This leaves only two possibilities for C^{-1}.

Suppose $C^{-1} = WCW$. Then $CWCW = I$, whence $CWC = W = WCWCW$, and $WCWC = I$. This provides much of the information we need to fill out the multiplication table. If the latter is to contain only the initial six elements, the remaining possibilities for C^2 are WC and WCW. But $C^2 = WC$ leads to $C = W$. So $C^2 = WCW$, from which it follows $WC^2 = CW$, $WC^2W = C$, and $C^2W = WC$. Thus one society with $W^2 = I$, $WC \neq CW$, and the minimum possible number of six clans has the multiplication table given below. Figure 24(a) is the diagram for this society.

·	I	W	C	WC	CW	WCW
I	I	W	C	WC	CW	WCW
W	W	I	WC	C	WCW	CW
C	C	CW	WCW	W	WC	I
WC	WC	WCW	CW	I	C	W
CW	CW	C	W	WCW	I	WC
WCW	WCW	WC	I	CW	W	C

The only other possibility for a six-clan society of this sort comes from setting $C^{-1} = C$. Then $C^2 = I$, and $C^2W = W$, so that $C(WC) = WCW$ must be true by elimination, since $C(WC) \neq WC$. The relevant rows of the multiplication table, which is uniquely determined by $C^2 = I$ for the six-element group, are

.	*I*	*W*	*C*	*WC*	*CW*	*WCW*
C	*C*	*CW*	*I*	*WCW*	*W*	*WC*
W	*W*	*I*	*WC*	*C*	*WCW*	*CW*

and Fig. 24(b) is the diagram. This latter group is just the group of all permutations of three elements, often called π_3. These two societies are so simple that their graphs could have been found by trial and error, but the reader can see that a rather different approach is needed than that used for first-cousin marriage societies.

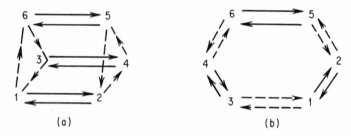

Fig. 2.24. The two smallest paired-clan marriage societies: (a) $C^{-1} = WCW$; $C^3 = I$; (b) $C^{-1} = C$; $CWC = WCW$. Here $WC \neq CW$.

Types of Second-Cousin Marriage with Sister Exchange. Hereafter only types 9–16 in Fig. 5 will be called second cousins, since types 1–8 are in classificatory kin terms either siblings or first cousins. In paired-clan marriage societies marriage can be said to be always by sister exchange, since male ego's wife must be a clan sister of the man who marries ego's own blood sister. If ego is the male in diagram 9 of Fig. 5, and he marries his female second cousin of type 9, it is obvious that diagram 10 can schematically represent the relation between ego's wife's brother and ego's sister, who also can marry. The horizontal line connecting grandparents in second-cousin diagrams hereafter will be understood to mean they are in the same clan though not necessarily siblings "by blood."

It is also clear algebraically that if type 9 second cousins can marry, type 10 second cousins can marry: if $M_9 = W$ then $M_{10} = M_9^{-1} = W^{-1} = W$, and conversely, since $W^2 = I$. Similarly, second cousins of type 11 can marry if and only if those of type 12 can, where $W^2 = I$ or $W = W^{-1}$. M_{14} is identical with M_{15} if $W^2 = I$, and M_{13} is identical with M_{16}. Moreover M_{13} is the inverse of M_{14} and M_{15} the inverse of M_{16}, when $W^2 = I$. Hence any one of the four types of second cousin 13, 14, 15, and 16 can be marriageable if and only if all three of the other types are too. All these statements are conditional. Sister-exchange marriage $(W^2 = I)$ is not a sufficient condition for any kind of second-cousin marriage.

Some additional condition on W and C is required to specify second-cousin marriage in paired-clan societies. In these societies one kind of second-cousin marriage is allowed if and only if at least one other kind is. It is natural that the additional condition should be a simple extrapolation of the commutivity law, $WC = CW$, which specifies bilateral marriage for first cousins given $W^2 = I$. The simplest reasonable extrapolations one can think of are

$$WC^2 = C^2W \tag{A}$$

and

$$(WC)^2 = (CW)^2. \tag{B}$$

($W^2C = CW^2$ would be an inane candidate for extrapolation of $WC = CW$ simply because $W^2 = I$ by definition.) In fact, given $W^2 = I$, Eq. (A) is the necessary and sufficient condition for bilateral second-cross-cousin marriage of type $9 + 10$; $M_9 = C^{-2}WC^2$ from Fig. 5, and if $M_9 = W$ then $WC^2 = C^2W$ follows, and conversely. Equation (B) is the necessary and sufficient condition for types $11 + 12$. Even more interesting, a cross breed of Eqs. (A) and (B),

$$WC^2 = (CW)^2, \tag{C}$$

is the necessary and sufficient condition for marriages both of types 13 and 14 and of types 15 and 16. That is, from Eq. (C) it follows that $M_i = W$ and conversely, where $i = 13, 14, 15,$ or 16. Also, if

$$WC^2 = CWCW, \tag{C}$$

then

$$C^2 = WCWCW$$

or

$$C^2W = (WC)^2, \tag{C'}$$

an alternate, completely equivalent form of condition (C).

Equations (A) and (B) can be true simultaneously. Suppose (A) and (C) are both true. Then

$$(WC)^2 = C^2W = WC^2;$$

so

$$WC = C;$$

so

$$W = I,$$

which violates Axiom 6. Suppose (B) and (C) are both true. Then

$$WC^2 = (CW)^2 = (WC)^2;$$

so

$$C^2 = CWC,$$

which leads to the same contradiction. When $WC \neq CW$ and $W = W^{-1}$

there are precisely four kinds of society with second-cousin marriage: either Eq. (A) above holds, or Eq. (B) above, or both Eqs. (A) and (B), or Eq. (C). These four kinds are described in Table 2.2. In a given kind of second-cousin marriage a girl can be in any one or all of the relationships to male ego shown in the fourth column. To be eligible as a spouse in one of these four types of society a girl must be a clan sister to all the second cousins listed as eligible spouses, even if to our way of thinking she is not "really" a second cousin by actual blood relation.

Type	Necessary and sufficient conditions	Eligible spouses for male ego among his second cousins	Code numbers in Fig. 5 for eligible spouses
$A + B$	$WC^2 = C^2W$, and $(WC)^2 = (CW)^2$	FMBSD FFZSD MMBDD MFZDD	9 10 11 12
A	$WC^2 = C^2W$	FMBSD FFZSD	9 10
B	$(WC)^2 = (CW)^2$	MMBDD MFZDD	11 12
C	$(WC)^2 = C^2W$ [or equivalently, $(CW)^2 = WC^2$]	FFZDD MMBSD FMBDD MFZSD	13 14 15 16

Table 2.2. The four types of second-cousin marriage with $W^2 = I$, $WC \neq CW$. In any of the types the same girl can be simultaneously related to a male ego by all the relations shown under "eligible spouses."

Second-Cousin Marriage: Type $A + B$. This one of the types of society with paired-clan marriage and second-cousin marriage is perhaps the simplest, and it is certainly the most important for describing known societies.

The order of W is 2, and as before let p be the order of C. Let q be the order of the element CW; i.e., q is the smallest positive integer n such that $(CW)^n = I$. In any system satisfying the eight axioms it follows that the order of WC is also q. For $(CW)^q = I$ means $(CW)^{-q} = I = [(CW)^{-1}]^q = (WC)^q$, and conversely; so there is a contradiction unless the order of CW equals the order of WC.

Since $WC^2 = C^2W$, for any positive integers r and s, such that $s \geq r \geq 1$,

$$(WC)^r (CW)^s = (WC)^{r-1}C^2(CW)^{s-1} = (WC)^{r-1}(CW)^{s-1}C^2.$$

By induction a lemma is established:

$$(WC)^r (CW)^s = (WC)(CW)^{s-r+1} C^{2(r-1)}$$

or

$$(WC)^r (CW)^s = (CW)^{s-r} C^{2r}, \qquad \text{THE BASIC LEMMA.}$$

A special case is, for $s = q$,

$$(WC)^r = (CW)^{q-r} C^{2r}.$$

But then

$$WC = (CW)^{q-1} C^2 \quad \text{or} \quad W = (CW)^{q-1} C.$$

Since $W^2 = I$, any element of the group generated by W and C can be written as a succession of powers of C separated by W. That is, each element in any list of members with no repetition can be written

$$C^x W C^i W C^j W C^k W \cdots C^n W C^m.$$

Here $i, j, k, \ldots, n$ must not be zero or a multiple of p, for then

$$\cdots W C^p W \cdots = \cdots W^2 \cdots = \cdots I \cdots$$

and so that element would not be distinct from some other shorter element in the list. Furthermore, $i, j, k, \ldots, n$ will each in fact be unity if we choose to collect all possible powers of C at the right of any element in the list. For C^2 commutes with W. Thus if j is even, C^j can be combined with C^m, and the W's which bracketed C^j disappear and C^i is combined with C^k, and so on.

Consequently a list without repetition of all elements in the group generated by C and W can be chosen so that any element can be written as

$$C^x WCWC \cdots CWC^t$$

where x is either zero or 1 and t can have any value, say $0 \leq t < p$. Let $x = 1$; those elements can be written

$$(CW)^j C^t, \qquad 0 \leq j < q.$$

Elements in which $x = 0$ can be written as

$$(WC)^k WC^t, \qquad \text{where } 0 \leq k < q.$$

But by the lemma above

$$(WC)^k = (CW)^{q-k} C^{2k}.$$

Hence elements with $x = 0$ can be reduced to

$$(CW)^{2q-k-1} C^{t+2k+1}.$$

That is to say, any element in the group generated by C and W can be written as

$$(CW)^j C^t, \qquad 0 \leq j < q, 0 \leq t < p.$$

From the lemma above

$$I = (WC)^q (CW)^q = C^{2q},$$

so that $2q$ must be a multiple of p; say $2q = bp$, b an integer > 0. Next suppose p is odd: $p = 2p' + 1$. Then

$$W = WC^p = WC^{2p'+1} = C^{2p'} WC.$$

Premultiplying by C,

$$CW = C^{2p'+1} WC = WC.$$

But $CW \neq WC$ by hypothesis so that p is even, or $p = 2p'$.

For the first time consider the implications of the remaining condition of the three defining Type A + B societies; namely $(CW)^2 = (WC)^2$. Suppose q is odd, or $q = 2q' + 1$. Then

$$(CW)^q = I = (WC)^q \quad \text{or} \quad (CW)^{2q'} CW = (WC)^{2q'} WC.$$

But

$$(CW)^{2q'} = ((CW)^2)^{q'} = (WC)^{2q'},$$

so that $CW = WC$, contrary to hypothesis. Thus q is even, or $q = 2q'$. Consider a further application of the lemma above:

$$(WC)^{2p'} (CW)^{2p'} = C^{4p'} = C^{2p} = I.$$

But then

$$(CW)^{4p'} = (CW)^{2p} = I.$$

Thus $2p$ must be a multiple of q, or $2p = dq$. The integer d must be positive since p is an order.

In sum, p and q are even, $p = 2p'$ and $q = 2q'$, and further $p = dq'$ and $q = bp'$. That is, $2q = bp = bdq'$. Thus

$$bd = 4.$$

There are only three solutions for positive integers b and d:

$$b = 1, \quad d = 4; \quad \text{i.e.,} \quad p = 2q,$$
$$b = 2, \quad d = 2; \quad \text{i.e.,} \quad p = q,$$
$$b = 4, \quad d = 1; \quad \text{i.e.,} \quad q = 2p.$$

To summarize the results thus far, any element in the group generated by W and C for systems of Type A + B can be written as

$$(CW)^j C^t,$$

the order q of CW is even, the order p of C is even, and either $q = 2p$ or $q = p$ or $p = 2q$. Clearly, if $q = 2p$, q is a multiple of 4; and if $p = 2q$, p is a multiple of 4. The list of distinct elements in the group generated by W and C can be still further simplified. $(CW)^2 = (WC)^2$, and by the lemma above

$$(CW)^4 = (CW)^2 (CW)^2 = (CW)^2 (WC)^2 = C^4,$$

or more generally

$$(CW)^{4j} = C^{4j} \quad \text{for any } j.$$

Hence any element can be written as C^t, CWC^t, $(CW)^2C^t$, or $(CW)^3C^t$, although these are not necessarily distinct for all $1 \leq t < p$ in any Type A + B system.

To go further, a subclassification of Type A + B is needed. Define y as the lowest power of (CW) which equals any power of C: let $(CW)^y = C^a$, $1 \leq a \leq p$. Clearly $y \leq 4$, and $q \geq y$. Suppose $y = 4$. Then there are $4p$ elements in the group. Certainly $(CW)^4 = C^4$; so a can't be greater than 4, but perhaps $a < 4$. Then $C^4 = (CW)^4 = C^a$ so that $C^{4-a} = I$ or $4 - a$ is a multiple of p. Since p is even, a can only be 2, and then p must be 2. Since $(CW)^4 = C^4 = I$, $q \leq 4$ but also $q \geq y = 4$; so $q = 4$ and $p = 2$ if $a = 2$, given $y = 4$, and there are $n = 8$ clans. The remaining possibility given $y = 4$ is $a = 4$, p can be any even number $p \geq a = 4$, and there are $4p$ clans; i.e., n must be 16 or some larger multiple of 8.

Before deriving the multiplication tables for groups in which $y = 4$, consider the other possible values of y, the minimum power of WC which equals any power of C. Then $y = 1$ is forbidden because otherwise

$$CW = C^j$$

and therefore $CW = WC$, contrary to hypothesis.

Next, $y = 3$. Then $(CW)^3 = C^a$, but also $(CW)^3 CW = C^4$, and thus

$$C^a CW = C^4,$$

or again $CW = WC$, contrary to hypothesis.

The only other possibility is $y = 2$, whence $(CW)^2 = C^a$. Thus

$$C^4 = (CW)^4 = C^{2a}$$

or

$$2a \equiv 4 \pmod{p};$$

that is,

$$2a = 4 + tp \quad \text{for some integer } t.$$

Let $t = 0$, then $a = 2$ or $(CW)^2 = C^2$, from which $CW = WC$, contrary to hypothesis. If $t \geq 2$, then $a > p$, which is impossible. Thus $a = 2 + p'$ is the only possibility for $y = 2$; i.e.

$$(CW)^2 = C^{p'+2}$$

Suppose p' is odd; then let $p' + 2 = 2e + 1$. Thus

$$(CW)^2 = C^{2e+1};$$

so

$$WCW = C^{2e}.$$

Hence both $CW = WC^{2e}$ and $WC = C^{2e}W$. But $WC^{2j} = C^{2j}W$; so if p' is odd, $WC = CW$ contrary to hypothesis. It follows that when $y = 2$

$$(CW)^2 = C^{2(p''+1)}$$

where $p = 4p''$, and p'' is a positive integer. The order of (CW), q is determined implicitly by the relation as either p, $2p$ or $p/2$. The number of clans $n = yp$ is any multiple of 8 for $y = 2$ as well as for $y = 4$.

Consider the multiplication of the standard list of elements for $y = 2$ and $p = 4$, and thus $q = 2$ and $n = 8$; namely, I, C, C^2, C^3, CW, CWC, CWC^2, CWC^3. $(CW)^2 = I$ yields $CWC = W$. Hence

$$C(CW) = WC^2 = CWC^3,$$

and so on. The relevant two rows of the multiplication table are

$\cdot$	I	C	C^2	C^3	CW	CWC	CWC^2	CWC^3
C	C	C^2	C^3	I	CWC^3	CW	CWC	CWC^2
$W = CWC$	CWC	CWC^2	CWC^3	CW	C^3	I	C	C^2

The corresponding diagram is Fig. 25. Observe that the multiplication table is uniquely determined for Type A + B systems by a given p for $y = 2$.

It is a bit more complicated for $p = 8$ and $y = 2$ to specify the product of two elements in terms of a third element in the standard list of group elements generated by W and C. Since $p = 8$, $a = p' + 2 = 6$, or $(CW)^2 = C^6$, and thus $q = 8 = p$. By the fundamental lemma

$$WC = (CW)^{q-1}C^2 = (CW)^6 (CW)C^2 = C^{18}(CW)C^2 = CWC^4.$$

Hence $W = CWC^3$. Thus for example

$$C(CW) = C^2W = WC^2 = (WC)C = (CW)C^5,$$

and

$$(W)(CWC) = (CWC^3)(CWC) = CW^2C^5 = C^6.$$

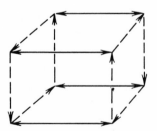

Fig. 2.25. One of two societies with eight clans of Type A + B: $WC \neq CW$, $W^2 = I$, $WC^2 = C^2W$ and $(CW)^2 = (WC)^2$. Here $y = 2$.

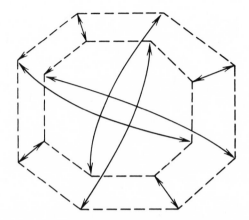

Fig. 2.26. Diagram of the Type A + B society with
$y = 2$, $p = 8 = q$, $a = 6$ and $n = 16$. The relevant
multiplication table appears below.

The relevant two lines in the multiplication table are shown below and a
diagram of the society is shown in Fig. 26:

.	.	I	C	C^2	C^3	C^4	C^5	C^6	C^7
	C	C	C^2	C^3	C^4	C^5	C^6	C^7	I
$W \equiv CWC^3$	CWC^3	CWC^4	CWC^5	CWC^6	CWC^7	CW	CWC	CWC^2
	.	CW	CWC	CWC^2	CWC^3	CWC^4	CWC^5	CWC^6	CWC^7
	C	CWC^5	CWC^6	CWC^7	CW	CWC	CWC^2	CWC^3	CWC^4
$W \equiv CWC^3$	C^5	C^6	C^7	I	C	C^2	C^3	C^4

Return now to the only other variety of Type A + B society, that with
$y = 4$. In the special case $a = 2$, $p = 2$ and $q = 4$ while $n = 8$. Then

$$(CW)^4 = C^2 = I.$$

By the basic lemma

$$W = (CW)^3 C.$$

Hence for example

$$(W)(CW) = CWCWCWCCW = (CW)^2 C^3 = (CW)^2 C.$$

The diagram can be drawn as in Fig. 27.

All other Type A + B societies with $y = 4$ have $a = 4$, or $(CW)^4 = C^4$.

Fig. 2.27. One of the two smallest Type A + B societies. Here $y = 4$, $a = 2 = p$, $q = 4$, $n = 8$.

Consider the smallest p, $p = 4$ so that $q = 4$ and $n = 16$. Then

$$C(CW) = WC^2 = (CW)^3C^3.$$

Also $\qquad C((CW)^2C) = WCWC^3 = (CW)^6 C^6 = (CW)^2C^2$

whereas $\qquad C((CW)^3C) = C^2(WC)^3 = (WC)^3C^2 = CW.$

The multiplication table and diagram (Fig. 28) are shown below.

.	I	C	C^2	C^3	CW	CW^1C	CWC^2	CWC^3
C	C	C^2	C^3	I	$(CW)^3C^3$	$(CW)^3$	$(CW)^3C$	$(CW)^3C^2$
$(CW)^3C = W$	$(CW)^3C$	$(CW)^3C^2$	$(CW)^3C^3$	$(CW)^3$	$(CW)^2C^3$	$(CW)^2$	$(CW)^2C$	$(CW)^2C^2$

.	$(CW)^2$	$(CW)^2C$	$(CW)^2C^2$	$(CW)^2C^3$	$(CW)^3$	$(CW)^3C$	$(CW)^3C^2$	$(CW)^3C^3$
C	$(CW)^2C$	$(CW)^2C^2$	$(CW)^2C^3$	$(CW)^2$	$(CW)C^3$	CW	CWC	CWC^2
$(CW)^3C = W$	CWC	CWC^2	CWC^3	CW	C^3	I	C	C^2

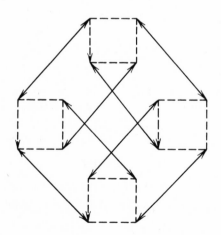

Fig. 2.28. One of the two A + B societies with $n = 16$, $p = 4 = q = y$.

In summary, there are societies of Type A + B only where the number of clans is a multiple of 8, say $8j$. For given $j > 1$ there are in fact just two societies,

$$\text{one with } y = 4, a = 4, \quad \text{and } p = 2j;$$
$$\text{one with } y = 2, p = 4j, \quad \text{and } a = 2(j + 1),$$

where y is the least positive power of CW which equals a power, denoted by a, of C: $(CW)^y = C^a$. Figure 1.13 of the previous chapter is the reduced role tree for Type A + B societies.

Type A Marriage. Everything derived above for Type A + B marriage down to the first use of $(WC)^2 = (CW)^2$ is valid here. A slightly different approach may be instructive, however. Societies with Type A marriage are defined as those in which second cousins of types 9 and 10 marry—that is, male ego may marry FMBSD and FFZSD as shown in Fig. 5—but not other types of second or first cousins. Thus $W^2 = I$, $C^2W = WC^2$, $WC \neq CW$, $(CW)^2 \neq (WC)^2$, and $(CW)^2 \neq WC^2$.

Certainly then $C^{2j}W = WC^{2j}$ for any integer j. A little experimentation shows how any element in the group can be written in one of at most two forms:

$$(CW)^j C^k \quad \text{or} \quad (WC)^j C^k.$$

Note that $(CW)^j = (CW)(CW) \cdots (CW) \neq C^j W^j$.

As always, let p be the order of C, $C^p = I$. Let q be the order of (CW) and q' be the order of (WC). Consider $(CW)^{q'+1}$. We can regroup the terms: $(CW)^{q'+1} = C(WC)^{q'} W = CW$, so that $(CW)^{q'} = I$. By a similar analysis $(WC)^q = I$. Assume $q' > q$: then $(WC)^q = I$ contradicts the assumption that q' is the order of WC. Assume $q' < q$: then $(CW)^{q'} = I$ contradicts the assumption that q is the order of CW. Hence the order of CW must equal the order of WC; call this common order q.

Next consider

$$(CW)^{-1} = WC^{-1} = WC^{p-1} \quad \text{and} \quad (WC)^{-1} = C^{-1}W = C^{p-1}W.$$

Let p be odd: $p = 2p' + 1$. Then

$$(WC)^{-1} = C^{2p'} W = WC^{2p'} = WC^{p-1} = (CW)^{-1}.$$

But then $I = (CW)^{-1}(WC)$, or $WC = CW$, contradicting a stipulated condition. Hence p must be even: $p = 2p'$.

A useful lemma is, for $q \geq s > r > 0$,

$$(WC)^r (CW)^s = (WC)^{r-1} WC^2W (CW)^{s-1} = (WC)^{r-1} (CW)^{s-1} C^2.$$

By induction it follows that for $s \geq r$

$$(WC)^r (CW)^s = (CW)^{s-r} C^{2r}.$$

Now $(CW)^q = I$, and thus $(WC)^r (CW)^q = (WC)^r$. But for any $0 < r \le q$ the lemma applies, so that $(CW)^{q-r} C^{2r} = (WC)^r$. This means that any element in the group can be written in the form $(CW)^j C^k$, where $1 \le j \le q$ and $1 \le k \le p$. Also $I = (CW)^q (WC)^q = C^{2q}$, so that $2q$ must be a multiple of p.

To go further we must develop a typology. Characterize a society with Type A marriage and p given, by the parameter z, where $(CW)^z = C^a$ for some $1 \le a \le p$ but $(CW)^c \ne C^k$ for any $1 \le c < z$, and k arbitrary. Since z is a minimum, each society can have only one value of z. Certainly every society does have a value of z since $(CW)^q = I = C^p$. Also note that $z \ne 1$, since then W and C would commute.

Any possible element in the group of a society can now be written $(CW)^j C^k$ with $1 \le j \le z$, and k as before. Suppose two of this list of possible elements are equal: $(CW)^j C^k = (CW)^{j'} C^{k'}$. Without loss of generality we set $j \ge j'$. Then $(CW)^{j-j'} = C^{k'-k}$. But $0 \le j - j' < z$. In order not to contradict the hypothesis, $j = j'$; i.e., $C^{k'-k} = I$. Since p is the order of C, $k = k'$ also, and so each element in the list is distinct. Therefore, the society has zp clans if z is the lowest power of CW which equals any power of C.

Not any value of a is possible. Since $(CW)^z = C^a$,

$$C(WC)^{z-1} W = C^a \quad \text{or} \quad (WC)^{z-1} = C^{a-1} W.$$

But $(CW)^{z-1} (WC)^{z-1} = C^{2(z-1)}$ by induction; so

$$C^{2z-2} = (CW)^{z-1} (WC)^{z-1} = (CW)^{z-1} C^{a-1} W.$$

Suppose a is odd: $a = 2a' + 1$. Then

$$C^{2z-2} = (CW)^{z-1} WC^{2a'} \quad \text{or} \quad C^{2z-2} = (CW)^{z-2} C^{2a'+1},$$

whence $(CW)^{z-2} = C^{2z-2-a}$, which contradicts the stipulation that z is the minimum power of (CW) which equals any power of C.

Therefore a must be even. Then $C^{2z-2} = (CW)^z C^{a-2}$. But $(CW)^z = C^a$; so $C^{2z} = C^{2a}$. Hence $2z \equiv 2a \pmod{p}$. In other words, $a = z - tp'$, where t is an integer such that a, which must be even, is between 2 and $2p'$ inclusive. Therefore for given z and p there are at most two possible values of a. For example, if for some integer f, $z = fp'$, then $t = f - 2$ or $f - 1$ and the only possible values of a are p' and $2p'$. If $z = fp' + 1$, only one value of a is possible, namely $p' + 1$, and even this is excluded if p' is even; since a must be even. If $z = fp' + 2$, then $a = 2$ with $t = f$ is always possible, and if p' is even, $a = 2 + p'$ with $t = f - 1$ is possible; no other values of a are allowed. More generally, if z is odd, p' must be odd.

Societies with Type A marriage (second-cousin types 9 + 10) are classified here in the first place by the parameter z. Then for each value of p, which must be even and such that $2q$ is a multiple of p, one finds at most two values of a. Given q, z, p, and a, one can at once construct the multiplication table of the group, and thus the diagram for the society. The order of CW, q, is necessary to calculate the multiplication table. Figure 1.11 of the previous chapter is the reduced role tree for Type A societies. It has not been proved that each value of the four parameters satisfying all the requirements above necessarily corresponds to a society satisfying all the axioms. Nor has it been proved that each set of q, z, p, and a yields a society distinct from those for the other sets.

Let $z = 3$, so that $q \geq 3$ necessarily. Consider $p = 2$. Then $a = 3 - t$. Since a must be even, and $1 \leq a \leq 2$, a can only be 2. Thus $(CW)^3 = C^2 = I$, and thus $q = 3$. The six distinct elements are written $I, C, CW, CWC, CWCW, CWCWC$. To find the relevant rows in the multiplication table we must know W. $W = WI = WC^2 = (WC)C$. But

$$(WC)^r = (CW)^{q-r}C^{2r} \quad \text{or} \quad WC = (CW)^{q-1} = (CW)^2.$$

Therefore

$$W = (WC)C = CWCWC.$$

Also note $C(CW) = C^2W = WC^2 = (WC)C = (CW)^2 C$. The relevant rows in the multiplication table are

$\cdot$	I	C	CW	CWC	$(CW)^2$	$(CW)^2C = W$
C	C	I	$(CW)^2C$	$(CW)^2$	CWC	CW
$W = (CW)^2C$	$(CW)^2C$	$(CW)^2$	CWC	CW	C	I

The diagram for this society is just Fig. 24(b), earlier derived by a different approach.

It is easy to see that one family of societies with Type A marriage is just the generalization of Fig. 24(b) to $2z$ links with alternation between dotted and solid arrows in successive links of the circular chain. That is, for any z let $q = z$ and thus $a = p$, and set $p = 2$. There is one exception: if $z = 4$, $(WC)^2 = (CW)^2$ and this society, already shown in Fig. 27, is Type A + B.

Type B Marriage. It is difficult to analyze the general case for MMBDD marriage (type 11 second cousins) with sister exchange. One would expect Fig. 24(a) to be a prototype, and there in fact $(WC)^2 = (CW)^2$. The next larger analogous society, for $p = 4$, is shown in Fig. 28, which represents a type A + B society since $WC^2 = C^2W$ also. Each figure parallel to Figs. 24(a) and 28 but with $p > 4$ represents a Type B society.

Type C Marriage. There seem to be no known examples of societies patterned on this ideal type. There must be at least twelve clans.

Paired-clan Societies without Second-Cousin Marriage. There seem to be no known societies patterned on an ideal type in which $W^2 = I$ but with no kinds of second-or first-cousin marriage. For such societies Fig. 1.8 of the previous chapter would be the general form of the reduced role tree.

2.11. Other Types of Marriage Systems

A society in which $WC \neq CW$ must contain at least six clans by an analysis parallel to that at the beginning of the previous section. In fact, if we interchange W and C then Fig. 24(a) clearly represents a society of the minimum size in which $WC \neq CW$ and $W^2 \neq I$, but rather $W^3 = I$. However, patrilateral marriage would be allowed, as can be seen by inspection of Fig. 24(a): in fact, with the solid arrows interchanged with the dotted ones, Fig. 24(a) is just Fig. 19. With only six clans, either $WC = CW$ or $CW = W^{-1}C$, unless $W^2 = I$.

There must be at least eight clans in a society with no first-cousin or paired-clan marriage, since any society with seven clans must have a cyclic group in which W and C commute. The only two noncommutative groups of order 8 are the quaternion group and the dihedral group, d_4. A society must have more than eight clans if it is not to be of Types I through IV.

It is natural to classify all societies of the residual Type V by what kinds of second-cousin marriage are allowed. As an example consider societies in which male ego can marry FMBSD and MMBDD (types 9 and 11) but no other first or second cousin. The simplest possibility is $C^2 = I$ and $W^3 = I$; i.e., the order of W is three. The diagram of this simplest society is given in Fig. 29. By inspection the reader can verify that $C^2 = I$, $W^3 = I$, $WC^2 = C^2W$, $(WC)^2 = (CW)^2$, but $WC \neq CW$, $WC \neq CW^{-1}$ and no other kind of second-cousin marriage is allowed. Figure 1.12 is the reduced role tree for such societies.

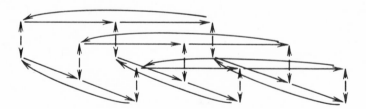

Fig. 2.29. Society without first cousin or paired clan marriage. Only two types of second cousins may marry male ego: FMBSD and MMBDD.

2.12. Numbers of Distinct Societies

Two systems are distinct if and only if there exists a type of relative who is in the same clan as ego in one society but not in the other. It has been proved there are no Type I societies (bilateral first-cousin marriage) with an odd number of clans and exactly two distinct such societies with each even number of clans. Societies with bilateral second-cousin marriage are most naturally defined as those of subtype A + B of Type IV; in such societies the number of clans n must be a multiple of 8, and for a given n there are exactly two distinct societies.

It is a simple problem in number theory to calculate for given n the number of distinct societies with matrilateral first-cousin marriage. Clearly the order p of C must be a factor of n: let $n = cp$. Each ordered pair of integers c and p which satisfy this equation have been shown to define a subclass of p distinct societies, corresponding to the p possible values of m in the equation $W^c = C^m$. In the special case $c = 1$, that is when all clans are in the same line of descent, there are only $p - 1$ distinct societies since $W = C^p = I$ would violate Axiom 6. Type II societies are defined as those with matrilateral first-cousin marriage but without sister exchange. When n is even the two societies with bilateral marriage, corresponding to $c = 1$ with $m = p/2$ and to $c = 2$ with $m = p$, should be subtracted from the count of distinct Type II societies. To summarize, the number of distinct Type II societies ($WC = CW$, $W^2 \neq I$) is

For n odd: (the sum of all distinct integers which are factors of n) $- 1$

For n even: (the same sum) $- 3$.

Note that if n is prime the number of distinct Type II societies is

$$n + 1 - 1 = n.$$

Patrilateral first-cousin marriage societies have also been categorized according to ordered pairs of integers c, p whose products equal the given number of clans, n, which must be even. As before $W^c = C^m$, but $c \geq 2$ and p must be even. If p is a multiple of 4 then m can be either p or $p/2$; otherwise m can only equal p. If $c = 2$ then $m = p$ corresponds to bilateral marriage for all even p, and must be excluded if one wishes to count only Type III societies.

The results of carrying out these counting procedures for all $n \leq 24$ and $n = 30$ and $n = 32$ are tabulated in Table 2.3. The results for Type V societies and for all subtypes of Type IV except A + B societies are incomplete and thus cannot be included.

| | First cross cousin | | | Second cousin: wife is MMBDD, FMBSD and ZHZ (Type IV, Subtype A + B) |
n	(Type I) Bilateral	(Type II) Matrilateral	(Type III) Patrilateral	
2	2	0	0	0
3	0	3	0	0
4	2	4	0	0
5	0	5	0	0
6	2	9	1	0
7	0	7	0	0
8	2	12	2	2
9	0	12	0	0
10	2	15	1	0
11	0	11	0	0
12	2	25	3	0
13	0	13	0	0
14	2	21	1	0
15	0	23	0	0
16	2	26	4	2
17	0	17	0	0
18	2	36	1	0
19	0	19	0	0
20	2	39	3	0
21	0	3	0	0
22	2	33	1	0
23	0	23	0	0
24	2	57	7	2
30	2	69	3	0
32	2	60	6	2

*Key:

Type I	*Type II*	*Type III*	*Type IV, Subtype A + B*
$W^2 = I$	$WC = CW$	$WC = CW^{-1}$	$W^2 = I$
$WC = CW$	$W^2 \neq I$	$W^2 \neq I$	$WC \neq CW$
			$WC^2 = C^2W$
			$(WC)^2 = (CW)^2$

Table 2.3. Number of distinct societies with *n* clans for four types of kin relation between ego and his wife.*

2.13. The Axioms Again

It is not necessary logically to the derivations carried out above to conceive of the clans as groups of people. Define a society as a set of *n* labeled points. A permutation on the set of *n* points means a transformation of the set which sends each point into one other point, i.e., a one-to-one automorphism. A permutation operator such as *W* or *C* can be represented equally well by an *n* × *n* matrix or as a directed linear graph. Axioms 1–5 in effect define two permutations, called *W* for wife and *C* for child, on a set of *n* points. Axiom 6 states that W is a permutation which does not transform any point into itself.

Axiom 7 is less simple. The permutations W and C generate a subgroup of the group of all $n!$ permutations of n objects, usually denoted π_n. Also, W and C each separately generates a cyclic subgroup of π_n. In this new language Axiom 7 states that the subgroup generated by W and C must contain for any pair of the n points a permutation which sends the first into the second. It follows that the group generated by W and C must contain at least n distinct elements. For there are only n entries in each $n \times n$ permutation matrix in the regular representation of the group (see appendix), and Axiom 7 requires that $\Sigma\, A_i \geq (1)$, where (1) is a matrix whose every entry is unity and the sum is over all distinct relation matrices generated by W and C. In the language of graph theory the graph of the n points, treating W and C links as indistinguishable and disregarding their directed nature, must be connected if Axiom 7 is to be satisfied.

Axiom 8 states that all the permutations generated by W and C are complete; i.e., they either leave no point unmoved or else all unmoved. In effect, Axioms 7 and 8 guarantee that no point can be distinguished from another by the effects of the W and C permutations upon them. Axioms 7 and 8 together say there must be exactly n elements in the group generated by W and C. In the language of graph theory any path, that is, any ordered sequence of W and C (directed) links, which forms a closed cycle beginning with one point will form a closed cycle beginning from any other point given Axiom 8.

There is an inverted way of looking at the effects of Axioms 7 and 8 which may be helpful. Consider any two permutations A and B defined by two 1-to-1 mappings of a set of n points onto itself. A and B will generate a group of say e elements. Then A and B can be taken as the W and C operators for an allowed society, but a society of e clans, where $e \neq n$, generally.

The need for Axioms 1–7 in defining a society with a consistent system of prescribed marriage is clear. Axiom 8 is not so transparent. It is only when one considers possible paths of evolution of prescribed marriage systems from classificatory kinship systems as in Chapter 1 that one sees why the homogeneity in structure guaranteed by Axiom 8 should emerge. Axiom 8 is equivalent to the statement that the collection of kin types equivalent to wife for any one man is the same as for any other man; without Axiom 8 one cannot speak of a common marriage rule for all men in the society. More generally, it was shown in Sec. 2.3 that, given Axiom 8, if two types of relatives of one man are in the same clan then the same two types of relatives of any other man must also be in the same clan.

2.14. Structural Duality—Matrilines and Patrilines

One example of dual structures has already been given: if the W arrows are changed into C arrows and conversely in Fig. 24(a), one obtains Fig. 19, and conversely. Our categorization of types of societies tends to conceal such dualities, for the focus of attention is usually on p, the order of C, and on what power of C can be equated to a lowest power of W. Thus often the order q of W is not specified explicitly, and the diagrams for societies of Types I–III are not drawn so as to show what q is. It is clear that there exists a dual structure in which W is interchanged with C for any society where $p \neq 1$. Except in Axiom 6, W and C are treated interchangeably in the axioms. There is little reason to investigate this kind of formal duality in detail, however.

C could have been defined as the transformation of mother's into child's clan as well as of father's into child's clan. In an actual society, people tend to think of some descendants in either a male line (patrilineal) or a female line (matrilineal) as part of the basic unit of society. Such a descent group can be perceived in terms of common name, common residence, and/or common inheritance rights, etc. In some societies one type of descent group is recognized as basic by one criterion and the other type by another criterion. There are also more complex cases of recognition of multiple descent lines. All this is formally irrelevant to the derivations presented above. Yet just as it is convenient to define C as the father to child transformation for patrilineal societies, it would be convenient to define C as the mother to child transformation for studying matrilineal societies, even though any society can be specified uniquely in either convention.

An interesting question is: what structures have the property that they are invariant under change from the matrilineal to the patrilineal convention? To put it more concretely, which of the allowed societies have a structure which would look the same to its members whether they chose to think of people grouped in matrilines or in patrilines? Figure 30, for a bilateral society with $p = 2$ parallel to that in Fig. 12, gives an example of such a society. In (a) the standard patrilineal notation is used whereas in (b) the dotted arrow is drawn from mother's to child's clan in the same society.

It should be clear that (b) is isomorphic to (a). (Imagine clans 1 and 3 interchanged in position by rotation through 180 degrees in a plane perpendicular

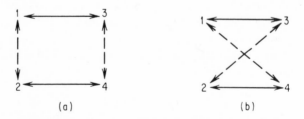

(a)   (b)

Fig. 2.30. Bilateral marriage society (Type I) with four clans and $p = 2$. In (b) each dotted arrow is drawn from a mother's clan to her child's clan, whereas in (a) the standard patrilineal notation is used.

to the paper.) Call this a *self-dual* structure. The general condition for such a structure is that if and only if

$$M(C^{-1}, W) = M'(C^{-1}, W)$$

then

$$M((C^{-1}W), W) = M'((C^{-1}W), W).$$

It is sufficient to take $M' = I$; i.e., a structure is self-dual when a path of specified structure in one convention is a closed cycle if and only if any path of the same structure is a closed cycle in the other convention.

Which clans in a society of a given type, drawn in our usual patrilineal notation, belong to the same matriline? If $p = n$, all clans are in the same "matrilineal line of descent" as well as in the same patriline. In most societies the number of matrilines will not equal the number of patrilines. The order of the element $C^{-1}W$, call it m, is the number of clans in each matriline; so n/m is the number of matrilines, just as n/p is the number of patrilines.

Consider bilateral marriage societies (Type I), for which n is even (Sec. 2.7). If n is a multiple of 4, then in *Case 1* where $p = n$ that society has one matriline as well as one patriline, while in *Case 2* where $p = n/2$ there are both two patrilines and two matrilines (see Fig. 30); moreover, any society with $n = 4j$ is self-dual. When n is twice an odd number, in *Case 1* there are two matrilines and one patriline whereas in *Case 2* there is one matriline and two patrilines; thus for $n = 2(2j + 1)$ the *Case 1* bilateral marriage society is the dual structure to the *Case 2* bilateral society. Two structures are defined as *dual* naturally if one is changed into the other when patrilineal notation is reinterpreted as matrilineal notation.

The situation is also simple for patrilateral societies (Type III) (Sec. 2.9). The parameter z for any Type III society is not only the number of patrilines but also the number of matrilines. Alternate clans in one patriline belong to the same matriline as the staggered alternate clans in the next adjacent patriline. The typical situation is shown in Fig. 31 for one of the two patrilateral societies with 16 clans and $z = 4$: members of the clan labeled a have

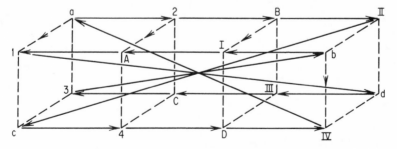

Fig. 2.31. One of two 16-clan patrilateral societies (Type III society) with $z = 4$. The four clans in each of the four matrilines are indicated by an ordered sequence of four alphabetical or numerical symbols. (See text.)

mothers in clan b, whose mothers are in clan c, whose mothers are in clan d, whose mothers are again in clan a; and similarly for the sets of clans labeled (A, B, C, D), $(1, 2, 3, 4)$ and (I, II, III, IV). In the other society with $n = 16$, and $z = 4$, $W^4 = I$, rather than $W^4 = C^2$ as in Fig. 31, but the only change in the arrangement of clans in matrilines would be the exchange of positions of b with d. It follows that every patrilateral marriage society is self-dual, which is consistent with the findings for bilateral marriage societies (*Case 2*, $n = 4j$).

Proofs of general statements about the number of matrilines and their dispersion through the patrilines are not important, since for any given society shown in our standard patrilineal notation it is easy to work out the identification of the specific matrilines. As example of how such proofs can be constructed if desired, however, there follows the proof of the above results for patrilateral societies. The operator $(C^{-1}W)$ in standard patrilineal notation transforms child's into mother's clan. Consider an odd power $(C^{-1}W)^{2j+1}$ written out as $2j + 1$ products of $C^{-1}W$. Collect all powers of W at the left. The last W on the right must be commuted with C^{-1} an odd number of times before it emerges at the left. Since $C^{-1}W = W^{-1}C^{-1}$ by definition of a patrilateral society, the last W on the right emerges as W^{-1} on the left, as does the third W from the right, and so on till the last W on the left. The second W from the left emerges as W on the left, however;

$$C^{-1}WC^{-1}W = (C^{-1}W)W^{-1}C^1$$
$$= C^{-1}W^{-1}WC^{-1}$$
$$= WC^{-1}WC^{-1}.$$

The net result, after cancelling reciprocal powers of W, is

$$(C^{-1}W)^{2j+1} = WC^{-2j-1}$$

in a patrilateral society. Therefore $C^{-1}W$ cannot be of odd order, for then W would equal a power of C so that $WC = CW$, the matrilateral marriage condition. On the other hand, the same derivation shows that $C^{-1}W$ to any even power $2j$ just equals C^{-2j}. Hence $C^{-1}W$ has the same order, p, as C, and thus there are the same number of matrilines as patrilines. Moreover $(C^{-1}W)^2 = C^{-2}$, whence a matriline is split between alternate clans in one patriline and the staggered set of alternate clans in the adjacent patriline.

The situation for matrilateral marriage societies is more complex. Consider the set of p matrilateral societies which has given values of n and c ($n = pc$). The number of matrilines ranges from 1 to p in any such set of societies, whereas the number of patrilines is always c. There is in a given society always at least one clan of a matriline in each patriline—unlike the situation in patrilateral societies—and every matriline has the same number of clans in each patriline.

One can define structures in many other ways and thus consider other kinds of duality. For instance, one could keep the patrilineal meaning for C and replace W by an operator M which converts mother's clan into child's clan. Specification of any two of the three operators C, W, and M is sufficient to identify the kinship structure of the society uniquely. Figure 19 in the standard C, W convention became Fig. 24(a) when W arrows replaced C arrows and conversely, but this was merely a formal duality with no plausible interpretation. The society represented by Fig. 19, with dotted and solid arrows meaning C and W operators respectively, is represented by exactly the same figure when dotted arrows instead mean the M transformation from mother's to child's clan; patrilateral societies are self-dual. But if the society shown as Fig. 19 earlier is represented using only C and M operators, then Fig. 24(b) describes that society. It might be appropriate to use C and M as the basic two operators to describe a society where children were permanently associated both with mother and with father, but spouses did not live together regularly or regard their direct relation as important. To avoid confusion the C, W, notation has been and will be used for every society throughout this book, but if for example one society is patrilineal and the other matrilineal it may be more meaningful to say they have the same structure when they are duals than that they look alike in the C, W notation.

2.15. Generations and Twisted Doughnuts

A *generation* is an ambiguous concept in kinship systems for which the eight axioms are valid. A man is in the pth generation above himself and in the pth generation below himself in the male line of descent to which he belongs. To avoid this ambiguity one could say a man is in the same generation as— though often much younger or older than—his WB, his WBWB, etc., and as his ZH, his ZHZH, etc. Even this is ambiguous, for often the order of W equals n, which means every person in the society is related to ego as WB in the first or the second, ..., or the nth remove. More generally, often several clans in the same patriline will be of the same generation by the criterion of being WB at some remove.

The basis of this ambiguity should be clear in terms of the discussion about closing role trees in the previous chapter. In the case of matrilateral marriage (see Figs. 1.5, 1.15, 1.17, and 1.18) the tree in the form of a two-dimensional net can be rolled up into a closed system of n clans as a logical consequence of the redefinition of roles attendant upon several particular marriages. In effect the net is first wound around the x axis (W axis) to form a cylinder, and then the cylinder is bent around to form a toroid or doughnut. However, since the closure is assumed to result from particular marriages of convenience there is no reason to assume the horizontal lines are kept distinct. Instead the cylinder will in general be twisted around its axis before its ends are joined to form a doughnut. In more formal language, this twisting corresponds in the algebraic analysis to the cases where in $W^c = C^m$ the power m is not p so that $W^c \neq I$. All the diagrams earlier for matrilateral societies satisfying the eight axioms could have been drawn in the form of doughnuts (with W arrows as arcs around the ring and C cycles as the cross sections of the doughnut). Analogous results hold for more complex role trees. An interesting and complex example is Type IV societies with Subtype A + B marriage: here the figures for sixteen-clan societies seem very complex, but careful inspection will show they both reduce to hunks of the role tree like a four-sided ladder in Fig. 1.13. Both can be drawn as types of twisted doughnuts, but with W arrows forming the cross section in one case.

2.16. Exchange of Women Relatives in Marriage

Sister-exchange societies have been defined as those in which $W^2 = I$; i.e., a man gets his wife from the clan from whom his sisters' husbands come. There are other types of women relatives to whom ego may feel close and over whom ego may have authority, apparently more so on both counts than with the sister in some societies. A useful way to classify societies is according to what female relative is given by male ego as wife to the men of the clan from whom ego obtains his wife, that is, to the brothers of ego's wife. There are always several equivalent ways to designate this female relative.

An alternative way to classify societies is possible where ego receives as wife the same type of female relative of the men from some other clan as he gives them as wife. Let $f(C, W)$, some sequence of powers of C and W, be the operator which transforms ego's clan into the clan of the woman relative given as wife to the other men. Then $f(C, W)W^{-1}$ transforms ego's clan into the clan of the other men. If the other men give the same kind of woman relative to ego, then $f(C, W)W^{-1}$ must transform their clan into ego's clan. Hence

$$[f(C, W)W^{-1}]^2 = I$$

is the necessary and sufficient condition for direct exchange between men in two clans of the same woman relative as wife, the two women in general being from two different clans not the same as either of the males' clans. In sister exchange $f(C, W)$ is simply I so that the condition is just $W^2 = I$, met in all bilateral (Type I) and paired-clan (Type IV) societies.

In what societies can marriage be viewed as the exchange by men from two clans of their daughters as wives to the other clan? For ego's daughter $f(C, W)$ $= C$; so the condition is $(CW^{-1})^2 = I$ or $CW^{-1} = WC^{-1}$. Those and only those bilateral (Type I) and patrilateral (Type III) societies in which $C^2 = I$ meet this condition; e.g. the societies in Figs. 19 and 30. Those and only those matrilateral (Type II) societies in which

$$W^2 = C^2$$

meet the condition. (See Fig. 16 for an example.)

Sister's daughter is another close relative over whom ego has much control in many societies. Men of two clans exchange their ZD's as wives if and only if $(W^{-1}CW^{-1})^2 = I$ since $f = W^{-1}C$; i.e., the condition is

$$W^{-1}CW^{-1} = WC^{-1}W.$$

All patrilateral and bilateral societies with $C^2 = I$, and only those, satisfy this condition. Those and only those matrilateral societies in which $W^4 = C^2$ satisfy it. Thus all bilateral and patrilateral societies in which $C^2 = I$ can be viewed as exchanging either daughters or sister's daughters as wives; but no matrilateral society can be viewed these two alternate ways, for then W^2 would have to be I.

Consider again the asymmetric exchange mentioned first: ego's exchange of a given female relative as wife to other men in return for their sister. Clearly the necessary and sufficient condition here is

$$f(C, W)W^{-1}W^{-1} = I \quad \text{or} \quad f(C, W) = W^2,$$

Suppose ego exchanges his daughter for the sister of another man. Then $f(C, W) = C$; so $C = W^2$ is necessary. No patrilateral marriage society meets this condition. The only bilateral society which does is the trivial one shown in Fig. 11. In all and only those matrilateral societies in which the order of W is n, the number of clans, as well as C equaling W^2, is daughter exchanged for sister.

Ego exchanges sister's daughter for the other man's sister if and only if $W^{-1}C = W^2$ or $C = W^3$. Again no patrilateral society is like this; Fig. 8 represents the only bilateral marriage society in which this is true; and for a matrilateral society to be like this the order of W must be n as well as $C = W^3$. It should be noted that in all these asymmetric-exchange societies ego necessarily sees not only one clan to whom he gives the specified woman relative as wife in exchange for their sister but also another clan to whom he gives his sister as wife in return for their giving him the specified relative of theirs as his wife.

In sum, there are a large number of ways to view a given society as the symmetric or asymmetric exchange between men of female relatives as wives. The appropriate procedures of derivation have been illustrated, and can be extended to apply to any culture in which some such view of exchanging relatives is found or suspected.

2.17. Biology and Kinship

Marriageability has been the focus of analysis. Always there are many different kin designations which simultaneously apply to a female relative who is an eligible spouse. This principle can be applied more generally.

When, for example, can the same boy be simultaneously MBS and FZS to ego?: if and only if

$$C^{-1}WC = C^{-1}W^{-1}C,$$

that is,

$$W^2 = I.$$

The same is true for daughter: a girl can be both MBD and FZD to ego if and only if $W^2 = I$. If $WC = CW$ the girl is also eligible as spouse to ego. If $WC \neq CW$ the girl cannot marry ego but nonetheless she is a bilateral first cross cousin. Take another example: when can the same person be MB and FZHF to ego? When and only when

$$C^{-1}W = C^{-1}W^{-1}C^{-1} \quad \text{or} \quad C = W^{-2}.$$

Another way to make the point is this: equations which identify a type of structure can be interpreted not only as fixing eligible spouses for ego but also as fixing what types of relatives with respect to ego are combined in the same person.

It is time to reassert the fundamental principle that the kinship relations analyzed here have no necessary logical connection with biological facts. For example, the term for father cannot imply an unambiguous biological relationship when a man we would call father's brother is called father, as in all classificatory systems. There is a more fundamental point, however. A kinship system satisfying the eight axioms could work perfectly well if the only source of children, that is of new persons to maintain the system, was a yearly boatload of baby orphans from Yugoslavia. Each orphan could be assigned at random to a particular man and woman as mother and father. The only requirement is that persons in the system accept that ego's kinship relations ramify through the society following the principle of cumulation of kinroles based on the initial nuclear family ties assigned the orphan ego. Presumably a mythology would evolve to give strong cultural support to the rightness of the scheme for allocation of Yugoslav orphans to particular couples and thence clan siblings and so on.

As they stand the models are static. Nothing is said about birth and death and their variable impact on the size and composition of different clans. No model is plausible as a stable description for a given tribe, whatever its explicit norms and terminology, if the average number of persons alive per clan at a given time is less than, say, 30. Age and sex distributions by clan are crucial in fixing bounds to the likely tenure of a given tribe's system and to possible directions of change.

Bibliographic Note

The single most useful mathematical reference is J. S. Lomont, *Applications of Finite Groups* (New York: *Academic Press*, 1959). His emphasis is on topics in natural science, since this is where most applications of group theory have been made. It is a very succinct work, so that it is not to be recommended as an introduction.

B. Higman in *Applied Group-Theoretic and Matrix Methods* (Fair Lawn, N.J.: Oxford University Press, 1955) writes in colloquial style and gives numerous simple examples in building up gradually to the basic ideas. The later sections of the book are quite technical, however.

Delightful illustrations and clear writing will be found in the elementary introduction *Galois and the Theory of Groups* (Brooklyn, no publisher given) by Mr. and Mrs. H. G. Lieber, who wrote *T. C. MITS*.

Much of the extensive literature by mathematicians makes no reference to representation theory, and so is only partially helpful. The chapter on group theory in *A Survey of Modern Algebra* (New York: Macmillan, 1948), by G. Birkhoff and S. MacLane, is very clear and precise, although not easy reading.

The reader will find most directly helpful the sections referred to in Sec. 2.1 above from *Introduction to Finite Mathematics* (Englewood Cliffs, N. J.: Prentice-Hall, Inc., 1957), by J. Kemeny, J. Snell, and G. Thompson.

Appendix

In the text it has been shown that the C and W permutation matrices which define the structure of a society of n clans with properties 1–8 generate a set of n distinct matrices A_i which are isomorphic under multiplication to an abstract group of order n. Next we show the converse: for any abstract group of order n which can be generated by at most two elements we can construct a representation of its elements as permutation matrices which defines an allowed society with n clans once C and W are identified with two elements sufficient to generate the group. Thus allowed societies can be categorized and specified in terms of the properties of pairs of elements which generate abstract groups.

Consider the multiplication table defining a group of order n: as an example we use π_3, the group of all six permutations of three objects:

	I	a_1	a_2	a_3	a_4	a_5
I	I	a_1	a_2	a_3	a_4	a_5
a_1	a_1	a_2	I	a_4	a_5	a_3
a_2	a_2	I	a_1	a_5	a_3	a_4
a_3	a_3	a_5	a_4	I	a_2	a_1
a_4	a_4	a_3	a_5	a_1	I	a_2
a_5	a_5	a_4	a_3	a_2	a_1	I

In writing general equations a_0 will stand for I. That entry in the table which lies in the row headed a_i and the column headed a_j is the element $a_i a_j$ formed by multiplying the two in that order. Each element of the group appears exactly once in each row since if $a_i a_j = a_i a_k$ then a_j and a_k are not distinct elements. Hence each row of the table is simply a permutation of the list of elements in (arbitrary) standard order written at the head of the table. Let A_i be the $n \times n$ permutation matrix which when multiplied by the standard list written as a row vector produces as product vector the permuted list exhibited in row i of the table.

After multiplication by A_i the place held in the standard list by element a_j is now instead occupied by the element which equals $a_i a_j$; more relevant, element a_j turns up in the place held in the standard list by the element $a_i^{-1}a_j$, since $a_i a_i^{-1} a_j = a_j$. Each permutation matrix has a fixed structure, of course; so when a vector of the n group elements not in standard order is multiplied by A_i, whatever element is in the standard position occupied by $a_i a_j$ is the one to turn up in the standard position of a_j, and so on. Consider the effect of successive application of A_k and then A_j to the row vector of group elements in standard order. First an element a_j is shifted to the standard position of $a_k^{-1}a_j$ and then to the standard position of

$$a_i^{-1}(a_k^{-1}a_j) = (a_k a_i)^{-1}a_j;$$

that is, the total effect is for each element to end up in the same place as if the permutation matrix corresponding to the element which equals $a_k a_i$ had been applied. Successive application of A_k and then A_i to a row vector is equivalent to applying the product $A_k A_i$ to the vector. Thus $a_r = a_k a_i$ if and only if $A_r = A_k A_i$. Hence the set of n matrices A_i under multiplication themselves constitute a group which is a faithful representation of the abstract group defined by the multiplication table for the elements a_i.

Let the abstract group be one that can be generated by either one or two elements. Label two of the elements which suffice to generate the group a_c and a_w, where a_w is chosen not to be the identity element. Then A_c and A_w are permutation matrices which define the marriage and descent rules— that is, the structure—of an allowed society of n clans, one which meets Axioms 1–8 of Sec. 2.2. The mere fact that A_c and A_w are permutation matrices satisfies Axioms 1–5, as shown in Sec. 2.2. If A_c has any diagonal entry, say the jth, equal to unity then A_c leaves a_j in its standard position; thus

$$a_c a_j = a_c^{-1}a_j = a_j,$$

or a_c is the identity element, so that A_c must leave all elements undisturbed, or in other words $A_c = I$, the identity matrix. The same argument is valid for all n of the distinct permutation matrices A_i, except that by stipulation A_w cannot be I. Thus Axiom 8 is satisfied. Consider the entry in the pth row and qth column of one of the n matrices, say A_k. It is unity if and only if $a_k a_p = a_q$. Now $a_q a_p^{-1}$ is necessarily an element of the group; so there must be a k such that $(A_k)_{pq} = 1$. A_c and A_w generate all n of the A_i matrices so that Axiom 7 is satisfied.

The regular representation of an abstract group is treated in many places in the literature: (1) Theorem 8, p. 136 of Birkhoff and MacLane, *op. cit.*

The language used is different from that of representation theory, however. (2) Higman, *op. cit.*, Theorem 1.6.5. (3) Lomont, *op. cit.*, pp. 54–55, gives a clear but succinct statement, with an example.

To prove there is only one inequivalent regular representation of a group, apply the theorems on pp. 58–59 of Lomont, *op. cit.* As indicated in the text, identification of a given two generators of a given group with C and W uniquely specifies a structure of an allowed society, since the numbering of the clans is arbitrary. There remains the question of whether two different pairs of generators for the same group (or for similar groups of the same order) can yield equivalent kinship structures, that is, two structures with the same partition of types of relatives into clans. A way to answer this question for each class of societies separately is demonstrated in the text; one need consider only the types of relatives in the clan containing ego's wife.

CHAPTER THREE

Models for Known Tribes

It is not to be expected that known tribes will conform with perfect rigor to the ideal models derived earlier for trees of classificatory kin roles and for closed structures of clans. Even if there were no deviations from some ideal model it would not be easy to decide how to identify the relevant model from anthropologists' reports. Terminology, norms, and possibly the tribe's own conscious interpretation of its kinship system may point to different models none of which are consistent with all known marriages.

The simplest hypothesis, which we shall always try first in analyzing a tribe's kinship terminology, is that ego uses each distinct kinship term to refer to one and only one "clan" of our abstract model, and conversely. To be more precise, this one-to-one relation need hold only for ego of a given sex addressing relatives of a given sex, since female ego may use a different set of terms from her brother and since usually ego will address a man and woman in the same clan by different terms; these divergences are discussed in detail for the Kariera. In most field reports kinship terminology is reported in detail but there are few genealogical data; so kin-term usage plus explicit marriage norms will be the primary basis for choosing the specific structure of clans which best fits a tribe, except for the Purums.

Where the structure of clans implied by the structure of kin terms is simple and unambiguous, as for the Kariera, we shall actually derive it algebraically using W and C operators. Where the structure is more complex and the fit with kin terminology more ambiguous, as for the Aranda, we shall simply propose the structure of clans and show how well it fits without showing the derivation process.

3.1. The Kariera

In 1913 Radcliffe-Brown published a field report, "Three Tribes of Western Australia," in the *Journal of the Royal Anthropological Institute* (**43**, 143–194). Each tribe at the time had less than one hundred members, most of whom spoke English and worked on sheep ranches. A less promising situation for obtaining valid accounts of functioning kinship systems is hard to imagine.

Yet the article is deservedly a classic. The accounts of the section system, kinship terminology, genealogical relations, and the connections among them are extremely lucid, especially for the first tribe described, the Kariera. Radcliffe-Brown's later books and articles on Australian kinship cannot be understood unless one has first read this article.

As is shown below, the account of the Kariera kinship system fits into our abstract framework perfectly, whereas field reports by other men on other tribes almost always have to be adjusted and reinterpreted. The clarity of the Kariera system is in fact suspiciously perfect. Other anthropologists, such as F. Rose (see Sec. 3.6), have pointed out grounds for suspecting the validity of the results. Detribalization was of at least 50 years standing, Radcliffe-Brown was a peripatetic observer, he reported no detailed data on genealogies, his knowledge of the language was imperfect, and so on. The excellent fit between Radcliffe-Brown's account and our abstract model is perhaps best viewed as a confirmation of our analysis not by data per se but by data as simplified and arranged into a coherent but nonmathematical system by a distinguished anthropologist.

Kariera is the name used by tribal members themselves as well as by their neighbors for the tribe, which has its own language and its own territory of about 3500 square miles along the coast of West Australia. The nuclear family of parents plus children is a distinct entity, especially in the consumption of food, in shelter, and in that it can and does travel independently. It will be shown, however, that the total kinship structure is not based on nuclear family ties as such.

All persons in the tribe except young children are addressed by relationship terms rather than personal names. The whole tribe is a body of relatives. Every person in the tribe must place every other person with whom he has contact into a relationship category and call him by the appropriate kinship term. Any person who cannot thus be placed is an enemy as well as a stranger and might be killed. A given kinship term is therefore applied to a whole category of genealogical relationships, which are equivalent from a structural point of view.

The Kariera tribe is divided into four named parts, which Radcliffe-Brown then called "classes." In our standard notation these are related as in Fig. 3.1.

However, a Banaka man, for example, cannot marry any Burung woman. "This class system can only be understood by a study of the system of reckoning the relationships of consanguinity and affinity" (p. 148). That is, the aggregate of types of relatives called by a given kinship term is not identical with one of the four "classes."

"As shown in the above list, each term is applied to a number of different relatives. Only some of those to whom the term is applied are mentioned in the list. . . . The list of relatives denoted by any one term could be extended indefinitely" (p. 149). Thus Radcliffe-Brown's interpretation of the application of kin terms agrees exactly with the fundamental requirement of our abstract models. He does not report the criteria by which he chooses which types of relatives addressed by a given kinship term are listed under the term in his tables, but there are more than enough types to carry out our analysis.

Maeli is the term for FF, FFB, MMB, etc. (whether ego is male or female). Thus these types of male relatives of ego are in the same clan. The matrix operator which transforms ego's clan into the clan of one of these relatives must equal the transformation operator for any other of the relatives. The equivalence of FF and FFB is built into our theory, of course, since brother-equivalence is the basic principle of any classificatory kinship system. FF and MMB are in the same clan if and only if

$$C^{-1}C^{-1} = C^{-1}WC^{-1}W,$$

or

$$C^{-1} = WC^{-1}W,$$

or

$$W^{-1}C^{-1} = C^{-1}W,$$

which is the necessary and sufficient condition for patrilateral first-cross-cousin marriage. When ego is male, Maeli also means SC and WMF. Hence

$$C^{-1}C^{-1} = CC \quad \text{or} \quad C^4 = I,$$

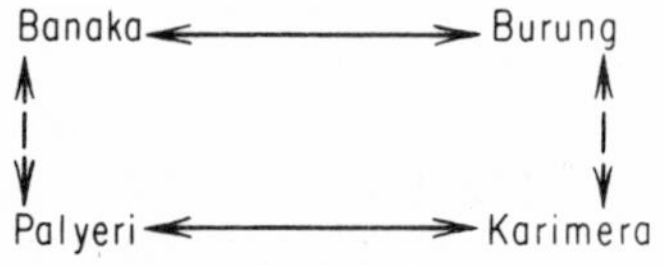

Banaka $\longleftrightarrow$ Burung
$\uparrow$ $\uparrow$
$\downarrow$ $\downarrow$
Palyeri $\longleftrightarrow$ Karimera

Fig. 3.1. Marriage ($\rightarrow$) and descent ($--\rightarrow$) relations among the four parts into which the Kariera are divided in the eyes of tribe members.

and thus the order of C, p, is either 1, 2, or 4. The equivalence of FF and WMF just yields again the patrilateral condition of semicommutativity:

$$W^{-1}C = CW.$$

Kabali is the term used by ego of either sex for FM, FMZ, MFZ, and so on. Thus

$$C^{-1}C^{-1}W = C^{-1}WC^{-1} \quad \text{or} \quad C^{-1}W = WC^{-1},$$

the commutativity condition for W and C, which is the necessary and sufficient condition for matrilateral cross-cousin marriage. If the data are to fit our theory it follows that W^2 must equal I and the Kariera must be a bilateral cross-cousin marriage society. For female ego Kabali also refers to HMM and SC. Equivalence of the former to FM again requires that W and C commute, and if we grant this then SC is equivalent to FM if and only if $C^4 = I$, a condition already obtained from Maeli.

Skip down Radcliffe-Brown's list to Kaga, the term applied by ego of either sex to MB and FZH. For these two to be equivalent,

$$C^{-1}W = C^{-1}W^{-1} \quad \text{or} \quad W = W^{-1} \quad \text{or} \quad W^2 = I,$$

which is a direct confirmation of the inference above that this must be a sister-exchange society. The only remaining question is whether p is 1, 2, or 4. The term for father is Mama, that for brother is Kaja (elder) or Margara (younger), and the term for son is Maiñga. Since all three are distinct, p should be 4: at least that is the simplest explanation.

There are a large number of other groups of relatives of a given sex, each identified with a specific kinship term by ego of a given sex. Without exception the operator equations implied by these new equivalences are either

$$WC = CW, \quad WC = CW^{-1}, \quad W^2 = I, \quad C^4 = I, \quad \text{(but } W \neq C^2\text{)},$$

or some more complex equation such as $WC^{-2} = CW^{-1}C$ which can be derived from the above four. Hence the Kariera function on the plan of a kinship system of eight clans, or aggregates of people, related through marriage and descent as shown in Fig. 3.2, which duplicates Fig. 2.12. For simplicity only male ego's terms for male relatives are shown in Fig. 3.2.

A figure exactly parallel to 3.2 could be drawn with the term for female relatives in a clan written below that clan's position. With two exceptions the term that male ego applies to a woman is different from the one he applies to her brother—and for that matter is different from the term applied to any male relative. The exceptions are that Maeli applies both to SS and SD and Tami applies both to DS and DD of male ego, which is reasonable since ego has no urgent reason to distinguish grandchildren by sex.

A woman usually applies to a person related to her through her father or mother the same term her brother uses. (The exceptions are related to the terms for cross cousins—see below.) This is consistent, since brother and sister

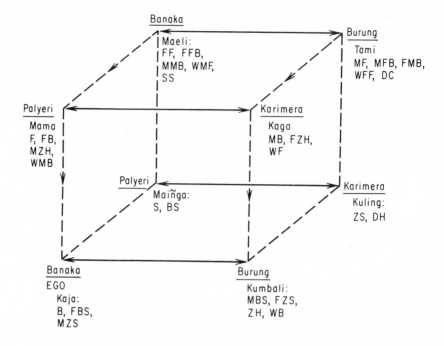

Fig. 3.2. Eight-clan model of Kariera tribe's kinship system. (See Fig. 2.12.) Two clans make up each "class" (section), the names of which are underlined. The male kin term associated with each clan, for male ego in lower left clan, is written below the clan, together with the types of relatives to whom it is applied. Data from Radcliffe-Brown (1913).

will find a given such relative in the same clan. A woman also calls her son by the same term, Maiñga, as her brother does, and similarly for the term for daughter, Kundal. But a woman's son is not in the same clan as her brother's son; so one cannot derive the operator laws of clan structure by equating the clans of relatives called by the same term unless ego is the same sex in all cases. For consistency, as one would expect, BS of male ego is Maiñga whereas to female ego ZS is Maiñga; also Kundal refers to BD for male ego but refers to ZD for female ego. Conversely, Ngaraia is ZD to male ego but BD to female ego.

The same laws for transformation operators are obtained by equating relatives called by the same term by female ego alone as are obtained using her brother as ego alone, but for the Kariera—as for most other tribes— erroneous results are obtained by mixing the two. Brother and sister are not in equivalent positions in the structure of kinship roles. In the Groote Eylandt case discussed later (Sec. 3.6) the sister calls every relative by the term her brother uses—e.g., she calls her son by the term her brother uses for ZS—but this is the exception rather than the rule. Brother and sister are not in equivalent positions in the structure of kinship roles, and usually the difference is reflected in the correlation between kin terms and clan membership.

Like male ego, female ego does not distinguish the grandchildren by sex. Her SS and SD she calls Kabali, the same term used by both male and female ego for FM, FMZ, and MFZ. Female ego's DD and DS are called Kandari, the term everyone uses for MM, MMZ, and FFZ. Observe that just as a male's SC are in the same clan as his FF, and his DC are in the same clan as his MF; so a woman's SC are in the same clan as her MF and her DC are in the same clan as her FF.

The crucial test of our model centers on the definition of eligible spouse. Ñuba is the generic term for eligible spouse used by both male ego and female ego. As our eight-clan model requires, for male ego MBD, FZD, BW, and WZ are all called Ñuba, while female ego calls MBS, FZS, ZH, and HB Ñuba. The men his sister calls Ñuba a man calls Kumbali, whereas the women he calls Ñuba she calls Bungali. This is an exception to the rule that a brother and sister use the same term for any person related through their mother or father. One might say that Kumbali is the "basic" term for MBS but female ego's relation to her potential spouses is so fundamentally different from male ego's relation to his MBS that a distinct term, Ñuba, is appropriate. For the same reason male ego deviates from the "standard" term Bungali for FZD and MBD.

The decisive evidence in favor of the eight-clan model is the exclusion of certain relatives from the category of eligible spouse. "A man's *kabali* may be only a few years older than himself so that marriage would be quite possible. It is, however, in the Kariera tribe, forbidden. The marriage rule of the Kariera is simplicity itself: a man may marry a woman who is his *ñuba*, but he may marry no one else. Thus we may say that in the Kariera tribe marriage is regulated by relationship, and by relationship alone" (p. 155).

It may be pointed out in passing that the last sentence in this quote from Radcliffe-Brown reveals the true meaning of his objections in later books and articles to the claim that marriage in Australian tribes with section systems is regulated solely by section membership. In this later work he says that marriage is always restricted to certain relatives defined by actual genealogical connections, but he always inserts the caveat to the effect that ego can marry classificatory equivalents, without ever defining classificatory equivalence. We now can infer that whether he realized it or not he defined classificatory equivalence in terms of one of our clan models, which are, after all, section systems. Normally, of course, the clan model for a tribe is more complex than any section system recognized explicitly by the tribe (or by anthropologists!), as in the case of the Kariera. Radcliffe-Brown's valid objections then boil down to a refusal to accept explicit section systems at face value, or else to the assertion that there is no clan classificatory system which encompasses all the members of a given tribe. Therefore his basic objection in the long paper [*American Anthropologist*, **53** (1951), 37–55] attacking Lawrence and Murdock's analysis of the Murngin tribe [*American Anthropologist*, **51** (1949), 58–65], an objection to their derived section system, does not make sense. This question will be considered again later, but now back to Radcliffe-Brown:

"A man applies the term *ñuba* to the daughter of any *kaga* and any *toa*. He applies the term *kaga* to his mother's brother and the term *toa* to his father's sister. Therefore it is obvious that by the above-stated marriage rule a man may marry the daughter of his own mother's brother or of his own father's sister. . . . Indeed we may say that the proper person for a man to marry, if it be possible, is his own first cousin. In the genealogies collected by me I found that in nearly every case where such a marriage was possible it had taken place" (p. 155).

Each person in the tribe falls in one of the eight clans, and any ego addresses all the men in one clan by the same kin term even though the genealogical connection of some to him may be very remote, and similarly for women. Each term has, however, a primary or specific meaning. For example, if a native is asked who his Mama is he will invariably give the name of his actual father (or if the latter is dead he may give the name of his foster father, who is usually the father's own brother). Radcliffe-Brown relied on this fact in collecting genealogies. Only in one case is there a separate term corresponding to the primary meaning: a man calls his own wife Nguranu rather than simply Ñuba.

Although natives retain detailed knowledge of real genealogies, they can and do deduce relationships from classificatory data alone. For instance, if man C is Mama to man A and Kaga to man B then all parties will deduce that A and B are Kumbali to each other. When a stranger comes to camp the first question he is asked is, "Who is your Maeli?" Then questioning continues until some person can be identified who is in a known classificatory relation to the stranger and in a known classificatory relation to one of the tribe members. From this base point the correct classificatory relations of everyone in the camp to the stranger can quickly be deduced and when he comes into camp all present will be introduced to him by the kin term which describes their classificatory relation to him. Radcliffe-Brown reports, "I watched two or three of these discussions in West Australia."

A male must look to his Kaga whose daughter he hopes to obtain as wife. His primary Kaga is his own MB, who may be his own FZH also since the exchange of sisters in marriage was a common custom. To say it another way, his Kaga's wife could be both his own FZ and his own MBW. Thus ego could marry a girl who was both his own MBD and his own FZD, which is consistent with our eight-clan model with bilateral marriage.

Any daughter of any Kaga was eligible as spouse to male ego, however. Normally parents would arrange marriages while the children were young. It was natural for a boy's parents to first try to arrange marriage with the daughter of the father's own sister and/or of the mother's own brother. The boy would give presents periodically to his potential wife's father. However, even where arrangements had been made with his own MB and/or FZH the normal practice was for the boy to also give presents to more distant Kaga who had daughters. The girl promised him might elude him through death or a variety of other causes and it was only sensible to take precautions.

A man's mother-in-law was taboo to him among the Kariera as in so many other tribes. He could not speak to her, look at her, or have any social dealings whatsoever with her. If they were in the same camp he would sit with his back to her.

Toa is the kin term male ego applied to WM, as well as to FZ, and MBW. Radcliffe-Brown makes a special point of the fact that the "mother-in-law" taboo applied equally to all women called Toa. This reinforces the conclusion that marriageability was determined by clan membership rather than by actual close genealogical status as cross cousin. It should be mentioned that when a man got too old he could apply the term Yumani (not used for any other female relative) to women earlier called Toa and could legitimately behave in a more relaxed way toward them.

Conversely, a woman had to avoid all men in the clan containing her BS, DH, and HZS, and in fact she used the same term Toa for them that they used for her. A woman had no need to avoid her FZ, HM, or MBW, however, so she called them not Toa, but a distinct term, Yuro. Similarly, a man had no need to avoid his ZS or DH; so he called them not Toa but a distinct term, Kuling.

It may help to repeat now in a different form the discussion of the Kariera terms for siblings' children. The basic fact is that male and female egos use the same word, Maiñga, for son, and the same word, Kundal, for daughter. The children of male ego's brother are in the same clans as his own children and so are addressed by the same terms; similarly, female ego addresses her sister's children by the same two terms as her own son and daughter. However, the children of the sibling of opposite sex to ego's are in a different clan and require different kin terms; Ngaraia for daughter of sibling of opposite sex and Kuling for son of sibling of opposite sex. It is because $W^2 = I$, the sister-exchange condition, that it is appropriate that the same term is used for son (daughter) of the sibling of opposite sex to ego no matter which sex ego is. However, because of the special restriction on social interaction between mother-in-law and son-in-law categories, ZS of male ego is not equivalent to BS of female ego. Instead a new term must be found for the latter to replace Kuling; it is the term Toa.

The mother-in-law avoidance custom is symmetric; so it is appropriate that Toa is also the term male ego uses for FZ, WM, etc. From this point of view Yuro is the "basic" term for FZ, just as egos of both sexes call MB Kaga, and the only reason male ego does not use Yuro is that a distinct term is needed to single out the women he must rigorously avoid. Note that each spouse has two parents-in-law but only one of the four, the mother-in-law of the husband, is subject to any special taboo in this tribe.

It is worth repeating that none of the discussion in the preceding paragraphs is necessary to derive the clan structure, for which it is sufficient to consider the kin terms for relatives of one sex to ego of one sex in isolation. Derivations based on any one of these four sets of terms give the same four laws in W and C operators. It is satisfying, however, to also understand the reasons for the patterns of overlap among the four sets of terms. It is only when analyzing kin terms for tribes with more complex and ambiguous clan structures that this luxury will be foregone.

Three alternate kin terms were omitted above for the sake of simplicity. Male ego may use a term Bali as alternate for the term Ngaraia for females in the clan containing his ZD and SW (female ego uses only Ngaraia for her BD and SW). Male ego may address males in the clan containing his ZS and DH as Yaraija as well as Kuling. Finally, male ego may address his BW as Yarungu as well as Ñuba. None of these three alternate kin terms is used for any other kin category.

Relative age is relevant to term of address in most primitive tribes. The term Kaja shown in Fig. 3.2 is actually male ego's term only for men in that clan who are older than ego; classificatory brothers who are younger he calls Margara. The same is true for female ego. Similarly both male and female egos use the term Turdu for older classificatory sisters but the term Mari for younger classificatory sisters. In itself this usage is consistent with our model; one would expect characteristics irrelevant to the kinship structure to induce different kin terms for the same structural role when the role is "close" to ego in the structure. In a sense ego's calling his own wife Nguranu instead of Ñuba is an example of the same thing. The very existence of a distinct kin term for brother is incompatible, strictly speaking, with pure classificatory logic; this was discussed in Sec. 1.3, where a distinction was drawn between the use of kin roles for "public" or "structural" purposes of generating a structure of roles into which all persons could be fitted and the use of kin roles for "private" purposes, of regulating details of relations between particular roles.

Another aspect of the relation between usage of kin terms and the relative ages of the two parties concerned raises serious problems about the applicability of our model. According to Radcliffe-Brown if man A is a father in classificatory terms to man B, but yet A is younger than B, then the terms of address will be reversed: A calls B Mama whereas B calls A Maiñga. The same is true for the pair of terms Kaga and Kuling for males, and for the pair of terms Nganga and Kundal for females.

I submit that this usage, which Radcliffe-Brown does not describe in detail or relate to his other material, must be restricted to terms of address. Man A above must still think of man B as son, and conversely, when it comes to reckoning position in the kinship structure—for example, whenever a stranger is being placed or whenever eligibility of men and women relatives as spouses is being calculated. For this dependence of classificatory position on relative age would not only violate our model, but it would lead to chaos in any classificatory system of reckoning kin. Suppose in the above example man B is five years older than man A and man B has an own brother C who is ten years younger. Then if relative age is decisive Man B calls man A son while B's own brother calls man A father. Thus to man C but not to man B a daughter of a sister of A is an eligible spouse. The fundamental principle of brother equivalence would be destroyed: men B and C would no longer be equivalent in the eyes of their descendants. It is reasonable enough, however, that in face-to-face contact—that is, in the "private" aspect of role behavior—a young male ego should call an older one by the term for men of a generation preceding ego's in the older man's line of descent.

There is of course a fundamental ambiguity in the concept of generations in kinship systems described by closed structures of clans. Radcliffe-Brown asked his informants what FFF would be called. He was told Maiñga, the term for son. Also FFM would be called Ngaraia, the term ego uses for ZD. This is the answer required by our model. Radcliffe-Brown found no case of an actual "blood" FFF alive at the same time as ego and treated the question as a very recondite if intriguing matter. In a society built of closed rings (or a ring) of clans, however, there is nothing extraordinary about such equivalences from a formal point of view. One can argue that the order of C is likely to be at least four simply because of the cognitive dissonance involved in calling, say, one's own son and one's own father by the same term, but these considerations lie outside the formal structure.

It is worth repeating that the cumulations of terms for nuclear family kin to denote a type of relative addressed by a certain Kariera kin term are for our convenience. In the logic of the classificatory system itself terms such as FFF and S are not merely equivalent, they are indistinguishable. A native can, if he chooses, trace "actual" genealogical connections to another person, but this is in no way essential to valid placement of the other. Quite often, for example, a person from outside a tribe might marry into it, and for this purpose he is in effect assigned a clan. Whatever the rationality of the assignment, he thereafter has a perfectly well-defined kin relation with all other tribe members even though he has no genealogical connection with them whatever. And whoever is defined by the tribe as a son of his will take over the coordinated set of kin relations with all the tribe derived from being Maiñga to the man.

3.2. Hordes and Clans

Perhaps the most ubiquitous feature of Australian tribal life is the constitution of the local groups, for which Radcliffe-Brown coined the term *horde*. The horde is like an extended family based on patrilineal descent.

Males related in the male line of descent plus their wives and children constitute the horde. Apparently among almost all the tribes in Australia the size of the typical horde ranged from twenty-five to fifty (men, women, and children). Presumably when a horde grew bigger than this a new horde split off, clustered about one or more of the younger men. There is little systematic evidence on this process, although it is known there have been steady patterns of migration of hordes, signalled partly by fighting over territory.

The ecology of these hordes is interesting. Each horde has a local territory, the boundaries of which are very clearly defined except in directions where the land is so barren as to be useless. Depending on the productivity of the land and so on, the area occupied by a horde ranged from one to a few hundred square miles, corresponding to a population density of one person for an area of from two to ten square miles. Within its area a horde was peripatetic, either as a whole or in family units. A man hunted game while his wives and children collected plant food, insects, and small animals. Since a man stayed all his life in principle with the horde in which he was born and since a woman usually was betrothed well before puberty and often spent considerable time before marriage with her husband's horde, it is not surprising that both men and women had knowledge of the most minute details of geography and food supply in the horde's area. Each small point in the landscape had its own name, and certain trees, springs, hills, etc. were sacred totem sites to which various members of that and other hordes were mystically bound. It was more a matter of the land owning the horde than vice versa. Animal species were also identified with totems, all tribe members being members of one or more totems.

Totem membership and religious practices transcended tribal boundaries, and many of the more important religious ceremonies required the participation of more than one tribe. It should be remembered that in many cases the tribe is defined as such by the anthropologist observer, the natives not thinking of tribal divisions in so clear-cut a way. As far as anyone has been able to figure out until now there is no simple connection between the kinship system of a tribe and the pattern of membership in totems and religious practices. There are a good many data on both the latter—indeed usually more of the field reports are devoted to them than to kinship—but they will be ignored here since they do not seem to help in understanding the kinship system.

Without the permanent, clear assignment of males to the hordes in which they were born and thus to a well-defined area held in common, such clear and consistent structures of clans built out of classificatory kinship trees might not have been possible, or so one can speculate. What is the relation of the horde to the clan?

The horde is a concrete group of people with a manifest identity visible to all, and often it is designated by the name of some prominent feature of its landscape. The clan is an aggregate of people perhaps perceived only by the observer, although usually at least some groupings of clans, such as the four "sections" among the Kariera, are recognized by tribe members and given fixed names. Another alternative is that a tribe's members may be perceived as split into two groups, a clan belonging only to one or the other, such that the same relative term will be applied by members of each group to all the members of the other group. The two groups normally will be patrilineal moieties in a tribe where only two distinct lines of descent are recognized, as in the Kariera.

Classificatory kinship terms themselves are a device by which the same terms of relation are applied by each of a set of aggregates of people to the other aggregates in the set. It is perhaps natural that the term of relation between aggregates logically and empirically takes precedence over the fixed name for an aggregate. The analysis in the first chapter is an attempt to show how the existence of permanent aggregates of persons as clans in a kinship system can be explained as a result, not a cause, of the system of kinship relations recognized in a tribe.

The clan, or rather the cycle of clans of a line of descent, is not derived directly as a grouping of hordes, though the horde too is defined in terms of a common line of descent among its male members. Possibly the horde is the primordial grouping of people. Once men in the horde come to look outside it for wives the basis for patterned relations between hordes is laid. According to the analysis developed earlier, the recognition and formalization of kinship ties among individuals in different hordes, as a consequence of interhorde marriage, might have been the first step. The logical requirements for the assignment of all persons to mutually consistent roles in a single role frame, that of kinship, could have led to the evolution of a clearly defined system of classificatory kin relations. In such a system all people of the same sex in a given "generation" of a horde would occupy structurally equivalent roles.

Equivalence of persons within the same generation of a horde, in the context of a system of classificatory kin relations, would have immediate implications for the equivalence of one horde with another. Consider three hordes, A, B, and C. Horde A has obtained wives from horde B, which has obtained wives from horde C. If now horde C obtains wives from horde B, then to men in horde B hordes A and C are equivalent: both contain ZH. The clan structure is fixed to the extent that $W^2 = I$ thereafter if consistency is maintained. Which "generation" in horde A is equivalent to which in horde C is, of course, a matter of which men in A and C happened to marry which women in B: once one man in a horde marries a woman in another horde the equivalence of "generations" in the two hordes is defined in principle, and future marriages should follow this equivalence even though usually there will be a full range of ages at any given time among the women in a given generation of a horde. If, on the other hand, horde C obtains wives from horde A, a structure of clans based on three rather than the two lines of descent is required thereafter.

Consider still other hordes, D, E, ... As men in them look to hordes A through C for wives (and conversely) they will assume a place in the structure of classificatory kinship relations equivalent to one of the hordes A, B and C, if either C men have married B women or C men have married A women. There is no other possibility compatible with a consistent system of classificatory kinship relations other than for each successive horde to be "folded in" as equivalent to some original horde once a closed system of marriage relations is defined among the original hordes. Of course, if men in horde C married no women in A or B, the possibilities are more numerous. Call D the new horde into which C men marry. If D men marry A women a structure of clans in four lines of descent would be required. If D men married C women, on the other hand, then B men would become equivalent to D men—both would be ZH to C men; hence B women would be eligible spouses to C men, and since A men also marry B women they would become equivalent to C men, so that the four hordes would be grouped into two lines of descent, A and C versus B and D.

Given demographic variability, not to mention variability in individual taste and emotions, it is likely that over the years men of a given horde will have to look to many different hordes to find legitimate spouses; eventually all hordes will be folded into a structure of clans. The above analysis of the way in which concrete hordes become defined as equivalent in classificatory logic was oversimplified for ease of presentation. It really should be a repetition in different terms of the analysis in the first chapter. When two women from one horde are married by men from two other hordes not all the men in the latter become equivalent, but only the men in the same generation as the two husbands. In the classificatory system of kin roles only men in the same generation in a given line of descent are equivalent; that is, are in the role of alter with respect to one another. The preceding analysis therefore should have been in terms of generations—clans—rather than rings of clans. The clan structure of the Arunta, the next tribe to be analyzed, is an example where two men in different generations of one horde marry into two different hordes, each of which is forbidden to the other man.

It will be remembered that in some of the structures which satisfy the eight axioms all clans are in the same line of descent. A given horde can have live persons in each generation in its line of descent (i.e., in the ring of p clans to which it belongs), but if there are many generations this will not usually be the case, given the tendency of hordes to split after a certain size. When there is but one cycle of clans or line of descent in the classificatory structure, any man in any horde could find a wife in any other horde were it not for the fact that some generations probably are not represented in a given horde. The number of lines of descent is the number of groupings of hordes, where only one group will contain eligible spouses for a given man.

Radcliffe-Brown provides a rough sketch map of the distribution of hordes in the Kariera tribe's territory (p. 144). As one would expect, a horde tends to have as its nearest neighbors hordes which belong to the other line of descent. Nonetheless, some of the marriages will take place with distant hordes of the opposite line of descent, and presumably these will provide enough data on interconnections to make possible the calculation of what generation in one horde corresponds to what generation in any other. Radcliffe-Brown reports that different hordes often camp together for extended periods. This is a custom common in many tribes: sometimes the hordes join to perform religious ceremonies, and sometimes hordes are invited to share seasonal gluts of foods found in the host horde's land. In many tribes there is a custom for young men to make long pilgrimages before marriage: for adventure, for curiosity, to find brides, etc. There is also clear evidence for networks of trade among tribes extending more than a thousand miles, in several different parts of Australia. Certainly there are many occasions for some or all of a horde to meet other hordes in their tribe, enough for mutual identification of classificatory kinship among some minimum network of people sufficient to keep alive the knowledge of correct equivalences among the generations of the various hordes.

3.3. The Arunta

Often called the Aranda by compilers of surveys, this tribe was described most fully by Spencer and Gillen, whose choice of names, spelling, and other terminology will be respected here. During their extensive field work, carried out in bursts of several months during the late 1890's, the Arunta numbered about 2000. In the 1920's Spencer reinterviewed one of his original informants, who had since learned English, and revised his account of the kinship system in *The Arunta*, published in 1927. By this time the tribe was demoralized and numbered 400, but the new material consisted largely of revisions of genealogies and marriage norms. The reader should be familiar with at least the first four chapters of *The Arunta* if he wishes to understand the general nature of the social and ecological structure from which the description of the kinship system below is abstracted.

The Arunta themselves thought of their kinship system as one of eight "subsections," named as in Fig. 3.3, which is drawn according to the conventions used in the previous two chapters. The term *subsection* is used by Spencer and Gillen and most later anthropologists when describing a tribe with a kinship system in which eight distinct aggregates of kin can be discerned. *Clan* will continue to be used as in the previous chapters as a generic term for such distinct aggregates whatever their number.

Other people were not designated solely by subsection membership plus personal name by an Arunta tribesman. There was a set of classificatory kin terms. A large member of modifiers were used with the basic terms in a rather flexible way to indicate birth order and sex. Apparently, the modifiers for

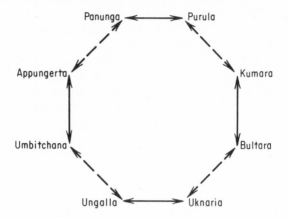

Fig. 3.3. Marriage (H→W) and father-to-child descent (F – – →C) connections among the eight named kinship subsections recognized by the Arunta tribe.

birth order did not enter the definition of eligible spouses and so they are ignored hereafter.

If the analysis of the previous two chapters is valid, there should apparently be a one-to-one relation between classificatory kin terms and clan membership. All men in a clan are alters, and all women in that clan are their classificatory sisters, according to the logic of the analysis. There are two reasons why the one-to-one relation should not be expected to hold empirically even though the earlier analysis be valid.

Classificatory kinship is an abstraction, both as the tribesman uses it and as the anthropologist should report it. Classificatory kin terms are a device to create, and are in turn a reflection of, an orderly structure of cumulated kin roles in which to group all tribesmen from any ego's point of view. Each tribesman is perfectly aware of who his "real" parents and other "close" relatives are. In the total set of kin terms reported one would therefore expect to find more than one term for men in ego's own clan and closely related clans. If the tribesmen are consistent, however, all but one of these terms for a given near clan should be used not as part of a classificatory system of terms but rather in an analytically distinct role frame for intrafamily relations.

On the other hand, if there are a large number of clans, especially in a "complex" structure, ego may not differentiate among them all by assigning a distinct kin term to each one. Ego is vitally concerned with the distinction between "wife's father" and "wife's brother's son" roles, for example, even if in Western terms concrete persons in those roles are very distant kin. However, ego need not in practice worry about any distinction between roles in alternate generations of a descent line of clans distant from him in the structure of clans. Let the people distant in this structure of classificatory kin fight their own battles about who is an eligible spouse or who has certain ritual rights over one of their number.

I propose that, subject to the above two exceptions, there is a one-to-one relation between Arunta kin terms and a certain kinship system of sixteen clans satisfying the eight axioms of the previous chapter. There is no reason why the Arunta themselves should recognize the full set of sixteen clans. It has been accepted by anthropologists that a tribe can function as if it had subsections, or a simpler set of kin aggregates, as a result of the operation of prescriptive norms of marriage expressed purely in terms of classificatory kin roles.

Figure 1.13 represents a reduced tree of kin roles which can be regarded as the general type of system of which the proposed sixteen-clan model is a special case. Any horizontal slice of Fig. 1.13 containing only one vertical "branch" in each of the four corner lines is equivalent to Fig. 3.3, the eight-subsection model. That is, if the father role becomes indistinguishable from son role in the logic of a classificatory system already simplified as in Fig. 1.13, one obtains the standard eight-subsection system. (Imagine the vertical segments in Fig. 1.13 to be dotted arrows, and then splay out the eight segments into a plane octagon to get Fig. 3.3.)

My proposal is that the Arunta classificatory system actually functions so as to maintain sixteen separate aggregates of people in the society. Specifically I propose that Fig. 2.28 describes the effective structure of the Arunta. Figure 2.28 is hard to visualize as a special closed form of the reduced tree in Fig. 1.13 and thus the parallel with Fig. 3.3 is obscured; so in Fig. 3.4 the sixteen-clan model proposed for Arunta kinship is redrawn. It can be seen that each clan in a pair related as father and son in Fig. 3.3 is split into two halves which alternate with the halves of the other named clan of Fig. 3.3, and each pair of clans in Fig. 3.3 thus has become a ring of four clans.

Spencer and Gillen report, for a male ego in the Purula subsection, the set of relatives called by each kinship term. Each kin term is applied by this Purula ego to persons in exactly one subsection; so Spencer and Gillen group the kin terms and associated sets of relatives according to subsection. Some kin term for each sex can be associated with each of the two clans of which a subsection is composed by our analysis; this association is reported in Fig. 3.5 for male kin terms and in Fig. 3.6 for female kin terms, where in both cases ego is male and has been placed in Purula clan 2.

That and only that set of relatives called by a given kinship term belongs in the associated clan in the model usually: this is the basic evidence in favor of our analysis. For ease of reference the set of relatives correctly placed is written in standard notation using capital letters—e.g., FZD—below the kinship term next to the location of each clan in Figs. 3.5 and 3.6. The relatives called by a kinship term associated with a clan who do not belong in that clan are discussed below. The reader can confirm correct placement by inspection, as well as by formal algebraic calculation. For example, in Fig.

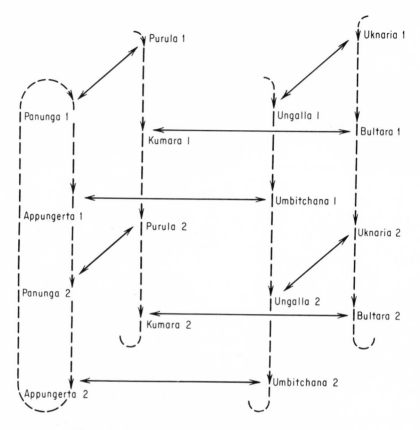

Fig. 3.4. Sixteen-clan model proposed to describe the effective kinship structure implied by Arunta classificatory kinship terminology. Names parallel those in Fig. 3.3. This model is simply a rearranged form of Fig. 2.28.

3.5 with ego in Pu 2, MB should be in Bu 1, and so MF should be in Uk 1, and indeed MF is called Chimmia. Spencer and Gillen also report kin terms for sets of relatives from the point of view of female ego: Fig. 3.7 reports these data for male relatives with female ego in Panunga 2 (the clan of wives for the male ego of Figs. 3.5 and 3.6).

There were ambiguities at crucial points in Spencer and Gillen's listings of relatives by kin terms and subsection membership (pp. 55–61, 1927 edition). Fortunately, kinship terms for a selection of twenty-one genealogical trees are also given (pp. 47–55), and they were used—after disregarding modifiers referring to birth order—to resolve some of the ambiguities. Additional relevant information was scattered through the text. Consider the ambiguities one by one.

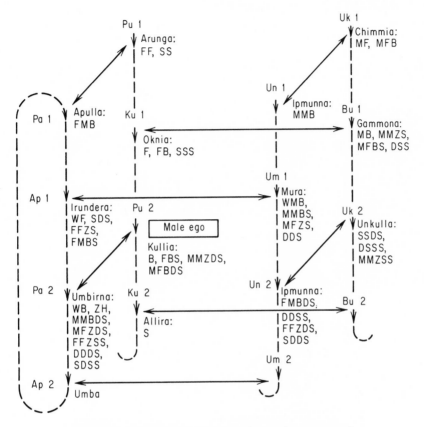

Fig. 3.5. Classificatory kin term for various types of male relatives in each of 16 clans: ego is male and a member of Purula 2 clan. Clan names abbreviated to first two letters of sub-section name — see Figs. 3.4 and 3.3. See text, points 1 through 10 for a discussion of ambiguities in this data, which is from Spencer and Gillen (1927).

1. Terms for spouse. In their list (item 6, p. 56) Spencer and Gillen group seven types of relative, including W and MMBDD, under "Anua or Apulla" and two types, FM and FMZ, under "Apulla or Yurapulla." All nine types are Panunga women for male ego in Purula. Footnote 1, p. 49, states "*Yura* is an affix used to denote female;" so we assume Apulla and Yurapulla can be used interchangeably for female relations of male ego. Also on p. 49 Spencer and Gillen describe, in a rather confusing way, how different kinship terms, a special case being Anua vs. Apulla, can be used for the same type of relative (in the same subsection) according to whether this relation to ego is distant or close, as judged either by residence or genealogical connection. It seems

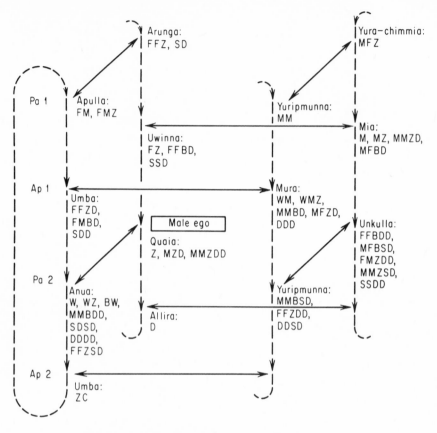

Fig. 3.6. Classificatory kin term for various types of female relatives in each of 16 clans: ego is male and a member of Purula 2 clan. Clan names abbreviated to first two letters of sub-section name—see Figs. 3.4 and 3.3. See text, points 1 through 10, for discussion of ambiguities in this data, which is from Spencer and Gillen (1927).

to me that variation in usage with closeness can be ignored for present purposes: such variation is superimposed on the classificatory kinship system as an added restriction and falls within the first exception cited above.

Spencer and Gillen do not report clearly the data on which their distinction is drawn between Apulla and Anua on the basis of closeness. Another interpretation, which can be regarded either as an alternative or as a supplement, fits into our model perfectly and agrees with the reported correlation of kinship terms. At the end of item 6 on p. 57 they say that "A man calls the son of an *Anua* woman *Allira* and those of an *Apulla* woman *Oknia.*" Also, only Anua women are eligible as wives to ego. This suggests that there are two clans in the Panunga subsection, women of one clan called Anua and eligible as wives and those of another called Apulla and not eligible. Figures

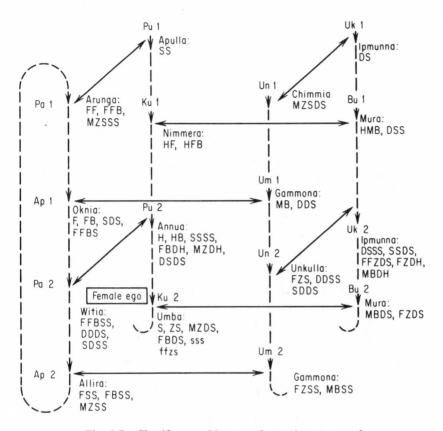

Fig. 3.7. Classificatory kin term for various types of male relatives in each of 16 clans: ego is female and a member of the Panunga 2 clan. Clan names abbreviated to first two letters of sub-section name—see Figs. 3.3 and 3.4. See text, points 1 through 10, for discussion of ambiguities in this data, which is from Spencer and Gillen (1927).

3.5, 3.6, and 3.7 are drawn in conformity with this, and the results are consistent: sons of Apulla women are clan brothers to ego's father and should be called Oknia whereas sons of all Anua women are classificatory sons to ego and should be called Allira. By this interpretation all seven female relatives listed under "Anua or Apulla" by Spencer and Gillen are classificatory Anua in contrast to the FM and equivalent classificatory relatives who fall in the category of Apulla. This interpretation is not inconsistent with the genealogical tree data.

In sum I propose that by the logic of the Arunta classificatory system there are two distinct clans of women in the subsection from which ego gets his wife, who can come from only one of the two clans. The clarity of the distinction is obscured because ego may call a few close blood kin, and women who reside nearby, by the classificatory term used for FM and her clan sisters even though in classificatory terms these few women are potential wives. This implicit taboo against marrying women close to ego will not lend to a modification of the classificatory system, because various male egos in say the Purula 2 clan will have different clusters of concrete women in the Panunga 2 clan close to them. Or at least there would have to be a proliferation of clans to a number comparable to the number of hordes, which are the local residence groups based on patrilineal extended families, before the classificatory kinship system could be modified to exclude all nearby women from the clan of women eligible as wives to ego.

Close relatives of potential spouses taboo to ego may be given the name of the "wrong" clan of their subsection to be consonant with the "wrong" name given to the tabooed potential spouse. Thus in Fig. 3.5, FMBS has daughters who are eligible spouses to ego in the logic of the classificatory system. Thus he should be in Appungerta 1 clan and be called Irundera, the term for WF. But if he be a close relative by blood or residence he will instead be called Umba and his daughter Apulla (p. 49) as if she were in Panunga 1 instead of 2: see male 23 in genealogy Table VII. The same usage applies for FFZS (males 17, 21, 26 in Table VI) and for SDS (male 11 in Table X).

Essentially the same ambiguity is found in the terms a woman applies to males in the subsection to which belong men eligible to her as spouses (see note below Table XX); it has been resolved the same way in Fig. 3.7. We return to a variant of this ambiguity of the classificatory term for spouse in point 8 below, where the clinching argument is developed.

2. As is clear from Fig. 3.5 the relatives FFBDS, MMZSS, and FMZDS should belong in the clan Uknaria 2 by our sixteen-clan model and indeed they can be called Unkulla, the sole term applied to other relatives in that clan such as SSDS and DSSS. However, these relatives can also be called Chimmia, according to Spencer and Gillen's list, which would place them incorrectly in the other clan, Uknaria 1, together with the relatives such as MF always called Chimmia which belong in Uk 1 by the model. This ambiguity, like the previous one, apparently results from assigning a few relatives close by blood or residence to the clan which is wrong by classificatory logic: on p. 49 Spencer and Gillen imply that daughters of an Apulla woman who marries a man residing near ego are called Winchinga, rather than the standard Uwinna (but sons of these daughters are inconsistently called not Chimmia but rather Unkulla). An equivalent distinction is shown in genealogy Table IV, in which it is specified that only actual immediate blood relations are shown in each branch of the tree: there all four women who are FZ are called only Winchinga, whereas in Table VI the four FFBD who are classificatory sisters to FZ can be called either Winchinga or Uwinna (presumably the former only when they are from a nearby horde).

A converse ambiguity is that DS, who should be called only Chimmia because he is in Uk 1, can also be called Unkulla, as shown either in the lists or in the genealogical tables. Neither of these ambiguities should be shown as an error in the figures, since like ambiguity 1 they refer to phenomena superimposed on the classificatory kinship system.

3. In their list Spencer and Gillen give the male term Umbana as an alternate term both to Umbirna, which should refer to WB and equivalent male relatives in Panunga 2 clan, and to Apulla, which should refer to FMB and equivalent male relatives in Panunga 1 clan: as always these assignments are predicated on male ego being in Purula 2 clan. (See Fig. 3.5.) However, in the many examples of both kinds of relatives given in the genealogy tables (VI, VII, etc.) the term Umbana is never used. It may be just a familiar diminutive of the term Umba for females in Appungerta clans (see below), and we ignore it hereafter and in the figures.

There is an error in the list of relatives under Apulla: DDDS and SDSS are included only under Apulla, although by our sixteen-clan model they should be in the same clan, Panunga 2, as WB, etc., and thus should be called Umbirna. In genealogy Table X, male 13 is SDSS to male ego and is called "Apulla or Umbirna"; in Table XI, male 15 is DDDS to male ego and is also called "Apulla or Umbirna." On the other hand, in the genealogy tables men who are FMB are always called only Apulla, and the men who are MMBDS etc., are always called only Umbirna. At worst, then, this seems to be an ambiguity of the type considered under point 2 above, and it is omitted from our figures.

4. There is a serious gap in Spencer and Gillen's data. They usually do not give terms applied to relatives traced through affinal ties, except for parent and sibling of spouse. In Figs. 3.5 and 3.6 neither any kinship term nor any relative is listed either for Umbitchana 2 clan or for Bultara 2 clan. One reason is that one must go through many classificatory kinship steps to find a relative related to ego solely through "blood" links (parent, child, sibling) who is in one of these clans, whereas for example in only four classificatory steps including affinal ties from ego there are relatives in Umbitchana 2 clan: WBSW, WBDH, etc.

In the special case of Appungerta 2 clan we know the classificatory kin term for males there is Umba, as shown in Fig. 3.5, even though none of the relatives there, only a few classificatory kin links from ego (WBS, etc.), are considered by Spencer and Gillen. This is because (as shown in point 1) men who belong in Appungerta 1 clan by classificatory logic but who are so close to ego that their daughters are taboo as spouses are known to be given the name Umba, and their daughters the name Apulla appropriate to the Panunga 1 clan.

5. Another ambiguity in the data is the use by male ego of the same term, Ipmunna, for males and females alike, both for relatives who belong in Ungalla 1 clan (e.g., MMB) and for relatives who belong in Ungalla 2 clan (e.g., FMBDS). None of these relatives is important to ego, we can argue,

and there is no need for him to differentiate between them. That is, although men who are classificatory MMB to ego may not legally marry women in Uknaria 2 (such as MFBSD), ego need not deeply concern himself with maintaining this distinction but rather can leave it to persons actually in those two descent lines, structurally the farthest removed from ego. This is the second general type of exception, discussed earlier, to be expected in actual application of the rigorous logic of classificatory kinship. The same ambiguity is also found for female ego, as shown in Fig. 3.7.

It may well be that the gaps cited in point 4 are really the same as this ambiguity, if only some examples of types of relatives belonging in Umbitchana 2 clan and Bultara 2 clan were included in Spencer and Gillen's data so that one would know if the same kin term were applied to both clans in the subsection. This suggestion is supported by Fig. 3.7, the set of male terms applied to the clans by a female ego in Panunga 2 clan. There both types of relatives belonging to Umbitchana 2 clan and types belonging to Bultara 2 clan are given, and in each case the kin term is the same as for the other clan of the subsection.

A more serious ambiguity occurs in the Appungerta clans in Fig. 3.6. Apparently ZC is called by the same term, Umba, as applies to FFZD and other types of relatives which belong according to the model to Appungerta 1 clan to which WFZ should also belong. It would seem so important to ego to distinguish between WFZ and ZC that he would apply distinct terms to them. One conceivable answer would be that women had little authority over disposal of their nieces in marriage among the Arunta and so this aunt-in-law was not important to male ego.

6. Spencer and Gillen must have made an error when they included SSDD in the list of relatives called Yuripmunna and associated with Ungalla 2 clan, given male ego in Purula 2. In genealogy Table X, female 10 is a SSDD of such a male ego and the term given for her is "Unkulla or Urumba," which corresponds to Uknaria 2 clan. Even in the eight-subsection model used by Spencer and Gillen SSDD of male ego in Purula must be in the Uknaria subsection. And finally, Spencer and Gillen also include SSDD under the term Unkulla for Uknaria women.

Spencer and Gillen or their printer also must have made a mistake in including FMZDD in the list of types of relatives called Chimmia. This would mean FMZDD should belong to the same clan, Uknaria 1 for male ego in Purula 2 clan, as MFZ, and this would contradict our sixteen-clan model, as is clear from Fig. 3.6. In Spencer and Gillen's genealogy Table VII three females, nos. 32, 34, 36, are FMZDD to a male ego who is in Purula 2 clan, and all three are called Unkulla, the term for Uknaria 2 clan, rather than Yura Chimmia. And in Table IX, females nos. 5, 6, 8, 9, 10, 12, and 13 are all MFZ and are all called Yura Chimmia, as is appropriate to Uknaria 1 clan to which they belong on our model.

7. There are three other contradictions between the grouping of types of

relatives by clan required by the model and their grouping by kin term reported in Spencer and Gillen's lists (and implicity in their genealogical tables). FFBZS is reported to be called Unkulla and is put in Ungalla subsection, for female ego as always in Panunga subsection. This contradicts even the standard eight-subsection model. Since B is redundant in FFBZS this type of relative cannot be found in the genealogy tables and I assume this must be a misprint. MMS is also reported as being called Unkulla, but even by the eight-subsection model it, like MB and DDS, must be called Gammona and be in Umbitchana subsection. Since MMS is equivalent in classificatory logic to MB, I believe MMS is a misprint also. Finally, MDS is reported by Spencer and Gillen to be called Witia along with FFBSS, etc., and to belong to female ego's own subsection. This is silly and must be another misprint.

8. We return to a variant of the ambiguity in point 1 in connection with Fig. 3.7. In their list Spencer and Gillen say that SS may be called either Anua or Apulla (and is in Purula subsection for female ego in Panunga subsection). But in genealogy Table XXI male 3 is SS to female ego in Panunga subsection, and the term given for him is Apulla only. This is in consonance with Fig. 3.6 where FM and FMZ are called Apulla only. Both the SS in Fig. 3.7 and the FMZ in Fig. 3.6 are in the same subsection as potential spouse to ego but in the other clan two generations above potential spouse in the same male line of descent.

A little reflection will show that this is crucial evidence in favor of our sixteen-clan model: there are some types of relatives in the same subsection as potential spouses according to the standard eight-subsection model who can never be married by ego. That is, according to the standard model classificatory SS are eligible spouses for female ego and classificatory FMZ are eligible spouses for male ego and yet in fact they are not allowed spouses since they can never be called Anua, the term for allowed spouse. In discussing ambiguity 1 above, I was showing how the application of the term Apulla to some and Anua to other persons in the same classificatory relation to ego could be explained as the superposition of nuclear family and residence taboos on the classificatory kinship system, so that this ambiguity did not invalidate either our sixteen-clan model or the standard eight-subsection model. Here I point out that the eight-subsection model should yield to the sixteen-clan model because only in the latter do we explain why all persons in certain classificatory relations to ego—whether they are "near" or "distant" cases of the relation—are excluded from marriage with ego even though they belong to the same subsection as allowed spouses. I cannot see how the eight-subsection model can be viewed as a complete analysis of the classificatory kin system of the Arunta unless it explains every rule which applies to all occupants of a given classificatory role whether they are "close" or "distant" kin to ego in nuclear family terms.

9. Two clear-cut contradictions between the sixteen-clan model and the data are shown in Fig. 3.7 by writing those types of relatives in small letters:

sss and ffzs in Kumara 2 clan. By the model sss and ffsz must be in Kumara 1 clan and therefore should be called Nimmera along with HF and HFB. Instead sss and ffzs are listed under Umba with S, ZS, etc. in Spencer and Gillen's list. In genealogy Table XXI, male 5 is SSS to a female ego in Panunga subsection and the only term given for this male is Umba, Similarly, in genealogy Table XIX, males 17, 21, and 26 are FFZS to female ego in Panunga subsection and again the only kinship term given for these three males is Umba.

10. Birth order for most kinship terms is indicated by added modifier words; e.g., a man's FFB is arunga kaindinia if he is the youngest brother and arunga arukalinia if the eldest brother. However, distinct words are used for siblings and their classificatory equivalents according to birth order. In the figures only the word referring to elder sibling is used. Thus kullia is given in Fig. 3.5 as the term for male siblings while actually younger siblings, male or female, are called itia or witia. This ambiguity does not affect the analysis of this kinship system into clans; indeed it is difficult to see how birth order could be used as an element in the structure of any classificatory kinship system.

In summary, only two clear-cut contradictions have been found between the data and the sixteen-clan model (see point 9 above). The eight-subsection model seems clearly inferior. Only the types of relatives actually reported by Spencer and Gillen to be called by each given kinship term are listed in Figs. 3.5, 3.6, and 3.7. Clearly the selection of these is rather haphazard, either because they were the only types that appeared in the concrete genealogical trees Spencer and Gillen collected or because the informants were only asked about these. Especially for male ego the types given include few affinal links, and many familiar types of relatives are not given. One of the main weaknesses of the standard model of eight subsections is exactly that one has no way of telling which of two terms used for, say, men in a given subsection should be applied to a type of relative not reported in the original data. For example, should WFFZS be called oknia or allira? One can decide "oknia" only from the sixteen-clan model. Yet in a consistent classificatory system ego must always know the answer to such questions. It seems to me plausible that the Arunta system functioned to maintain the sixteen distinct aggregates of people represented by the clans; certainly a population of 2000 was big enough, even without marriages into neighboring tribes. Other tribes are known which recognize four generations in each line of descent, and it seems the simplest adequate interpretation of the Arunta to assert there are four generations distinguished in each of the four lines of descent.

3.4. The Murngin

A Black Civilization (1937) is W. L. Warner's report of fieldwork from 1926–29 among the peoples of northeast Arnhemland. Tribal divisions are vague there as in most of Australia and Warner applies the term Murngin both specifically to the people in the central area studied most intensively and generally to the whole collection of peoples studied in an area of about 100 miles on a side, the tip and coastal islands of a flat peninsula of the north shore of Australia. The basic unit of social organization throughout the area is a group of males acknowledging common patrilineal descent identified with one or more water holes which play central roles in the mythology distinguishing the group. These men, together with their wives and children, normally total about 40 people and "own" or "belong to" an area of say 400 square miles usually contiguous to their water holes. Warner calls these groups *clans* (and reserves *horde* to denote more casual clusters of people gathering food together), but in conformity with previous usage *horde* will be used for his *clan* hereafter. A man never marries a woman from his own horde.

Warner's chart of the kinship terms used by male ego (p. 59) is reproduced here as Table 3.1. Later (p. 123) Warner asserts, "They follow a very simple rule: ego and his sister call all relatives by the same term. If ego calls a man or woman "kutara," she addresses them by the same term. This means that ego's son and daughter, whom he calls gatu, are also called gatu by his sister, while her children are called waku by him and by her. Ego's sister's husband calls her children gatu, and ego's sister's husband's sister would also call them gatu." Male ego can distinguish a brother from his sister where ego calls both by the same kinship term, say galle for mother's brother's children, by adding diramo to indicate a man or mielk to indicate a woman.

The novel feature of Murngin kinship terms as reported by Warner is that ZH, ZHZH, etc., lie in successive "lines of descent" which are distinct from the successive "lines of descent" in which lie WB, WBWB, etc., although all these relatives are in the same "generation" as ego. It is also unusual for five generations in ego's own line to be recognized by distinct terms. Warner's chart implies for each kinship term an indefinitely large number of relatives to which the term applies: not only should, say, FFBS be called by the same term (bapa) as F, which is true in all classificatory systems, but also for example MMBDD and FMBSD as well as MBD should be called galle mielk. In fact, Warner's chart is identical in structure with the plane grid of Fig. 1.5, which represents the tree of cumulated kin roles when reduced by identity between W and MBD roles.

Anthropologists generally have accepted the chart's implication that the Murngin classificatory kinship system is one based on matrilateral first-cross-cousin marriage, but there have been heated arguments over the exact nature of the system. Warner's chart of kin terms ends in mid-air three generations away from ego both on the ZH and the WB sides. One formulation of the central issue has been the question: what male kinship personality does ego's ZHZHZHZH marry and what female kinship personality does ego's WBWBWB marry?

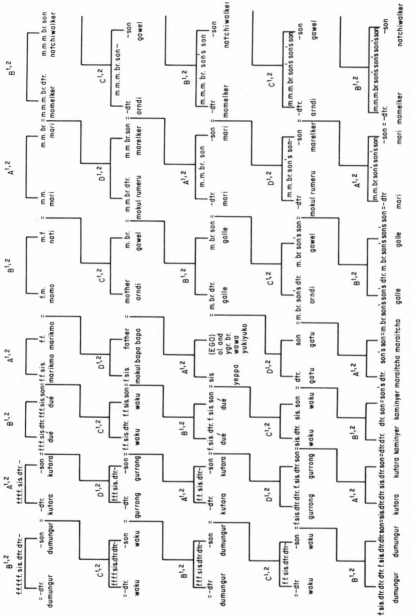

Table 3.1. Reproduction of Chart II, p. 59, in W. Lloyd Warner's *A Black Civilization*, New York, Harper and Brothers, 1937, by permission of the publisher.

Warner's answer is as follows (p. 115, emphasis mine):

At first sight, the enormous extent of a Murngin kinship system seems unexplainable and almost fantastic. There seems no reason for the spread of the lateral lines. *With the asymmetrical cross-cousin marriage system* three lines of descent are automatically created: ego's line, the mother's line (which is ego's marrying line), and the sister's husband's line. They must be recognized by the culture because all people are counted as relatives.

Shall there be recognition of a new line of relatives and the creation of a new set of social personalities? Or shall this additional line of kin be "thrown back" into one's own patrilineal line and called by the same terms as those found in each generation of ego's line? The latter expedient is used to set *the final limits on the Murngin kinship structure.* When the line beginning with natchiwalker in the upper right-hand corner of the kinship chart marries into the line at its right, this new line is again called the mari, mokul, marelker line to terminate the system.

If a consistent classificatory kinship structure has final limits, these limits and indeed the whole structure must look the same from the point of view of any (male) ego. From Warner's account, in some ego's eyes a man who is natchiwalker marries a woman called mari whose brother's line terminates the system because it is "folded into" the mari line to the left of natchiwalker. Thus the woman's brother marries the sister of ego's natchiwalker. This constitutes the exchange of classificatory sisters in marriage, whether viewed through the eyes of the original ego or of natchiwalker and his WB. In other words, bilateral rather than asymmetrical cross-cousin marriage is being practiced at the extreme right (and left) of the chart of kinship terms. But suppose the man originally in the role of natchiwalker is now taken as ego. In his eyes the whole system is rolled up into two classificatory lines of descent; for instance, a man the original ego called nati or galle is viewed by the new ego as a brother (or FF depending on the generation) since they both marry women called mari who are classificatory sisters. Thus to the extent that there is a consistent system of classificatory kinship among the Murngin, it is built of two distinct lines of descent.

Each person in the Murngin tribe belongs to one of eight aggregates and has a corresponding fixed name (male different from female) in addition to kinship terms applied to him which vary relative to the ego applying them. Dua is the general name given to one group of four aggregates and Yiritja the name for the opposite group: opposite because not only all people but also all living, all inanimate, and all intellectual objects are perceived as split between this dichotomy of Dua vs. Yiritja according to intricate criteria derived from the tribe's mythology. Persons who are Dua are all thought of as having at least remote ancestors in common in the male line of descent, and similarly for Yiritja; so these groups are patrilineal moieties in standard parlance. All men in a horde necessarily are in the same moiety.

Why not use the standard term "subsection" for the eight aggregates?

Father and son are never in the same aggregate, although always in the same moiety, as in every other known system with subsections. The strange thing about these Murngin aggregates as described by Warner (pp. 117–120) is that men who are classificatory brothers in the kinship system can be in either of two aggregates. In other words, there are four pairs of aggregates, called *sections* hereafter, such that all men who are classificatory brothers to each other in a section have an identical set of women from another section eligible as spouses and all have children in the same section. Warner calls the four sections A, B, C, and D: the marriage and descent relations between them are shown in Fig. 3.8.

For ego in section A his relatives are in the sections indicated by the same four letters in the Murngin kinship chart above: superscript numbers there indicate that a given kinship personality can be in either of the two aggregates in that section. Warner obscures the complete behavioral equivalence of the two aggregates in a section by emphasizing that the aggregate in its section that a child belongs to is determined solely by which aggregate in her section the mother belongs to. Some such arbitrary rule is necessary, since men of either aggregate in the section of her husband can legitimately marry her even though Warner vaguely claims that marriage to men in one of the aggregates is only an "alternate" form.

The Murngin division of all kin into four sections related as in Fig. 3.8 tends to imply bilateral cross-cousin marriage and a recognition of only two distinct lines of descent. This implication agrees with the collapse of seven lines into two lines of classificatory siblings found above to be implied by Warner's comments on the termination of the chart of kinship terms. On the other hand Warner speaks of a system of unilateral cross-cousin marriages and the chart of kinship terms seems to imply that.

Yet Warner nowhere reports any explicit norm against marriage with FZD, real or classificatory. (The basic analysis, pp. 57–58, assumes but does not assert such a norm. It is curiously elliptic prose.) He discusses in detail the behavior norms associated with each reciprocal pair of kin terms. It is perhaps revealing that the same reciprocal pair of terms for each other, dué and galle, are used by male ego and MBD as are used by male ego and FZD: of the latter pair it is the male who is called galle while of the former pair it is the female who

Fig. 3.8. Marriage (→) and descent (− − →) norms among the four sections into which the Murngin are divided. Sections A and D constitute the Dua moiety, while B and C are the Yiritja moiety.

is called galle. More important, Warner in the long sections on various combinations by sex in the Dué-Galle pairs (pp. 74–93) discusses the norms for male ego and his FZD only in a very brief and vague paragraph on p. 93 which sounds more like deduction than a report on field observations.

To resolve the question of asymmetry vs. symmetry in first-cross-cousin marriage among the Murngin it is essential to examine the interrelations of hordes in the kinship system. All men in a horde are split into groups of classificatory brothers who constitute successive generations in a patrilineal line of descent. This is the standard composition of the local group in Australian tribes with classificatory kinship systems. All the men may stand in known close genealogical relations through their fathers, at least if the horde be small. (Possible deviations from the standard among the Murngin are discussed later.) Warner names forty-three hordes in eight tribes in the Murngin area, and there were others, at least in the Burera tribe, he did not record.

Moiety, totems, water holes, location, and dialect are specified for forty of the hordes (pp. 44–51), and the other three hordes in the Yandjinung tribe are ignored below. From one to two thousand people thus are included in the area Warner studies.

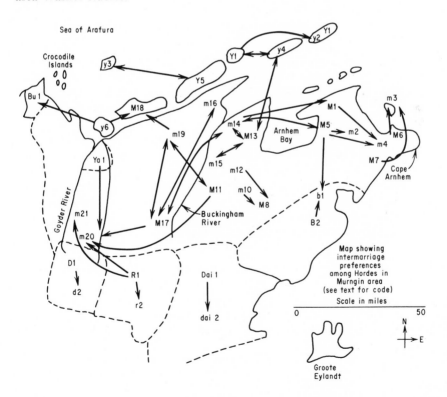

The most revealing data in the whole book are in a list on p. 28:

Below are listed the [hordes] which usually intermarry. This does not mean that these [hordes] do not also marry into other groups. It is felt, however, according to my informants, that the [hordes] listed in the right-hand column are the ones into which those listed in the left-hand column prefer to marry.

Records of actual frequency of marriage among hordes would be valuable. These expert opinions on marriage preferences among hordes, however, probably single out only relations which receive normative support in the society and have actually been realized in a number of concrete marriages by men of the horde to women of the other.

The map on the previous page represents preferred marriage of men in horde M1 to women in horde m4 by a directed arrow:

$$M1 \longrightarrow m4.$$

The letter(s) in the symbol designate the tribe to which the horde belongs according to the following code, in which the number of hordes in each tribe, by moiety, is also listed:

		Number of Hordes		
Code symbol	Tribe	Dua moiety	Yiritja moiety	Totals
M	Murngin	11	9	21*
Y	Yaernungo	4	2	6
B	Barlamomo	1	1	2
Dai	Dai	1	1	2
R	Ritarngo	1	1	2
D	Djinba	1	1	2
Ya	Yandjinung	2	2	4
Bu	Burera		1	1
	Totals	21	18	40

* Moiety not given for clan 9.

Warner's numbering of the hordes in each tribe is used. If a horde is in the Yiritja moiety its tribe code symbol preceding its number is in capitals; when the horde is Dua the tribe symbol is in small letters. The map is rough but preserves relative position.

In Warner's list one or more "choices" of hordes for wives is made by 23 hordes, and one or more choices received by 26 hordes. Only four of the 40 hordes are entirely omitted from the list. One or more choices of a horde to marry into are both received and made by 13 hordes. A total of 42 choices are reported; i.e., there are 42 arrowheads shown on the map. The largest number of choices made is four (by M17 and M5) and so is the largest number received (by m20).

The basic evidence for bilateral cross-cousin marriage is that 20 of the 42 preferences of one horde for marriage with the women of another are reciprocated; that is, ten of the 32 arrow shafts on the map have arrowheads at both ends. In all ten pairs at least one of the pair has preferences for more than one other horde, but it is reasonable to assume that some men from each horde marry women of the other horde in the pair. It is likely therefore that in classificatory terms some sisters of brothers in, say, horde m14 are married by brothers in horde M5 whose sisters are the wives of the brothers in m14; hence when succeeding generations in the two hordes marry each other their spouses are both FZC and MBC to them in classificatory terms.

One could argue that the men in one horde who marry women from the other horde in a reciprocal pair need not be in the same generation as the men in the other horde who marry women in the first horde. If some such scheme for exchange of women between staggered generations in two hordes were institutionalized it would not lead to bilateral first-cross-cousin marriage, but neither could it yield matrilateral cross-cousin marriage. In any case Warner's informants did not distinguish between generations in reporting marriage preferences among hordes. Moreover, from the data given a pair of hordes like y3 and Y5 may obtain wives from no one but each other.

If Warner's conception of asymmetrical marriage is valid there should be at least three distinct hordes in a ring of hordes passing wives around, and never two. In fact there are *no* complete rings of marriage preferences among hordes in Warner's data, except for the ten reciprocal pairs. Not only are reciprocal pairs found, but there actually seems to be a premium on them. One could construct a variety of null models of marriage choice among hordes, but by any of them—even those in which choices tend to be restricted to nearest neighbors—ten pairs of reciprocated choices would be well above the chance expected value. Also, one can see from the map that many of the reciprocal pairs, for instance M5 and m14, are separated both geographically and by intermediate hordes eligible for marriage as far as moiety membership is concerned.

Insofar as there is a consistent classificatory system of kinship among the Murngin it is a bilateral marriage system formalized in their section system. Any female in the appropriate section is an eligible spouse to ego as far as her position in the classificatory kinship system is concerned (except possibly for additional generation restrictions discussed later), and all such females are both MBD and FZD to ego in classificatory terms. This is the conclusion one draws from Warner's data by applying the general analysis of the logical nature of classificatory systems developed in Chapter 1 and later.

Nonetheless Murngin do have terms for the MBD and succeeding lines distinct from the terms for the FZD line and its further lines of descent. These terms are not used in a purely genealogical sense, for the chart of kin terms has no room for collateral lines, and so they exhibit some of the rudiments of a classificatory system. It is arbitrary whether men in one horde of a reciprocal pair apply terms in the MBD or the FZD line of the kin chart to persons in the other horde, for both terms are legitimate in classificatory logic. Presumably all the men follow the same choice and it is likely they use MBD terms, since many of the marriages with the other horde are to actual blood MBD but probably few with actual blood FZD.

It seems probable that Warner's chart represents a flexible kit of kin terms which ego adapts to the particular circumstances of his horde. Consider an ego in horde m14, and suppose he chooses to call men in M5 horde by kin terms in the MBD (galle) line of the chart. Then it is natural to call men in the m2, the m4, and the b1 hordes by terms in the MMB (mari) line, even though in classificatory logic they should be folded into ego's own line, the terms in which ego uses to address men of his own horde m14. Similarly ego in m14 assigns MBD (galle) line terms to men in M1 horde and mari line terms to men in m4 horde, the latter assignment being the same one he would derive by reckoning his relation through men in M5 instead.

This hypothetical ego in m14 could also use kin terms in the galle line for M13. He could then assign his own line of kin terms to y4, but more likely he would go on and assign mari terms to y4 and natchiwalker terms to Y1, whereupon if he bothered to assign kin terms to y2 at all he would have to use some expedient such as assigning the mari line again. Or ego could have folded Y1 into the same line of galle kin terms as M13, since both marry y4 and thus can be considered brothers, in which case y2 would still be assigned the mari line of kin terms.

It is inefficient for our hypothetical ego in m14 to make no use of the dué (FZD) side of the chart, but there is no horde that marries m14 without giving wives in return. Perhaps M17 has married into m14 more often than vice versa; so ego might well choose to apply dué line terms to M17, kutara terms to m19, dumunger terms to M11. If he reckoned his relations with m20 through M17 directly he would fold m20 into his own line m14; if he reckoned through M11, ego would have to fold m20 into the same line of kin terms as for m19, kutara. Ya1 and R1 hordes could then either be equated with the dué line for M17 or the dumungur line for M11. Ego would have to fold Bu1 into M18 and thence into the dué line for M17; y6 would merge with m19.

In short, men of a horde with as many reciprocal marriage connections as m14 have an enormous variety of ways in which they can allocate unilateral kin terms to other hordes. An ego in M1, on the other hand, would necessarily assign galle terms to m4 and dué terms to m14. M1 ego could reckon kin terms with other hordes through m14 in a variety of ways, but his only choice through m4 would be to fold M5 into the kin terms for his own horde and then reckon through the eyes of M5 men. Since M5 men assign galle terms to m2, m4, and b1 it would seem likely they would choose to assign due terms to m14, with whom they actually stand in bilateral relation so that m14 is both dué and galle to M5 in classificatory logic. This choice by M5 men is consistent with the choice assumed earlier for m14 men to apply galle terms to M5 men. Presumably, whatever the variety of terms possible between two hordes, each will come to use a line of terms which is the reciprocal in the kin chart of the line of terms applied by the other to it.

The analysis has been hypothetical since the marriage preference data are not complete, and no data are given on the kin terms used for one horde by another, but the line of argument is made clearer through these examples. The implications of reciprocated marriage between hordes have been developed on the assumption that all men in the same generation in a horde were classificatory brothers. On p. 17 Warner mentions that an ego sometimes may apply kin terms in the mari (WBWB, MMBSS) and kutara (ZHZH, FFZDS) lines to other males in his own horde. It would seem to follow that the men called mari by the original ego must use the kutara line terms not only for the original ego and his brothers but also must fold into the kutara line the men the original ego had called kutara. Thus men in his horde whom an ego would not call brothers would be classified as brothers to ego by a third group of men in the horde, and vice versa. In effect this is a microscopic version of the original question posed: how does the kinship chart terminate? The only consistent resolution would be for the men original ego called mari in turn to apply mari terms to the men original ego called kutara. This would make sense only if the three lines original ego recognizes in his own horde each marry women in the same line in some other horde whose brothers in turn marry sisters of the "next" line of men in the original horde. Although theoretically possible, such an elaborate structure of relations within a horde seems unlikely. The effect of having distinct lines of kin recognized more than temporarily in a horde is to eliminate the significance of the horde as a unit in the kinship system. Male ego lives out his life in his horde, which is the core unit in both ecology and mythology, and it is hard to believe that he could keep straight the kin terms to apply to other hordes if not all the men in his own generation of his own horde were classificatory brothers to him. Certainly it is implausible that in all ten pairs of hordes with reciprocal preferences for marriage distinct lines of descent are recognized within each horde in just such a way as will prevent the men in any pair from standing in the classificatory relation of bilateral first cross cousin to each other.

Wrong marriages might at first seem the explanation of the existence of several lines of descent in one horde. Warner reports (p. 105) that other people call the children of a wrong marriage by the kin term appropriate to children of a correct marriage by the *woman*: "The father is thrown away." Thus sons of men in a horde can be given kin terms not in the same line as the term applied to their father. One strange thing in this procedure as Warner reports it is that everyone readjusts the kin terms applied to the *woman* in the wrong marriage to what it should be for a correct marriage to that man, even though the kin terms for the couple's children are adjusted to the woman's initial kin terms. Yet Warner says, "This simple arrangement always keeps the kinship system functioning smoothly."

Moreover, wrong marriages cannot create new lines of kin terms in the horde from the point of view of men in the horde. Warner earlier (pp. 26–27) reports that egos within a horde reckon descent of children through the father when a man in the horde marries wrong. Thus the child of a wrong marriage is reckoned by the men of his father's horde as B, S, F, etc., whereas the males in his mother's horde reckon him as ZS (waku) to them, and since the father and his horde line cannot be in the dué-waku line in the eyes of the mother's horde the boy is seen as in a different line. The operational implication would seem to be that this son of a wrong marriage can marry into his mother's horde but not other boys of his father's horde who see him and are acknowledged by him as brothers. It is hard to believe that such a situation can persist and lead to the institutionalization of a separate line in the horde of the original wrong father, a line which does not acknowledge itself distinct and yet has separate marriage rights in the eyes of other hordes.

The final question to be examined is how many "generations" in a line of kin terms are recognized as distinct in classificatory logic. In the outer two lines on each side of the kinship term chart of seven lines only adjacent generations are assigned distinct terms, the two terms being repeated in alternation up and down the line. All five generations have distinct terms in ego's own line, but one could argue that these distinctions reflect not the general classificatory structure but ego's desire to differentiate his personal relations to all generations he may live with in his own horde. In his W (galle) line ego calls both M and MBSD arndi, and he applies the term galle not only to his W (or MBD) but to the girl two generations below. A new term, momo (FM), appears only at the head of the line two generations above W.

A girl consummates marriage earlier than her brother of the same age, in Australia as here. She is married at puberty or even before (p. 76), whereas by Warner's account (p. 5) a boy at earliest would marry at 18, and the implication of polygamy would seem to be that on the average he won't marry until much later (see pp. 76–77). Hence ego will tend to be older than his MBD, which is consistent with her being a preferred spouse. Ego will continue to accumulate wives at a late age, however (p. 77), and it is entirely possible that his galle two generations below him in classificatory terms will be of an age to marry him. On the other hand it is unlikely, even allowing for the spread of ages in a classificatory "generation," that many of his momo (FM) will be enough younger than him for him to marry them.

If momo (FM) is distinct from galle in the classificatory system of kinship there must be at least six clans in the closed ring of clans constituting that distinct line of descent and by inference in all other lines too. The Murngin system has been shown to be a loose one in other respects and it is not plausible that six distinct clans are institutionalized. Also, Warner makes it clear (pp. 82–83) that sexual liaison between ego and momo is regarded with equanimity unlike liaisons with other female relatives, even those in the opposite moiety to ego; so momo is assimilated to galle. Instead, assume only two generations are distinguished: galle from arndi. But suppose a given ego calls all galle too old to be married momo, just as older brothers are called wawa while younger brothers are called yukiyuko, neither distinction being a part of the classificatory kinship system. When collecting data from various individuals, Warner would find most actual FM called momo by informants but few others, and he could well conclude that momo was a classificatory term. Ego could marry momo on classificatory grounds but wouldn't on age grounds; yet he would and does feel free to explore sexual life with her.

By the mirror of this argument kaminyer may merely be a term denoting a dué who is younger than the woman speaking. Thus it is possible that the elaborate chart of kinship terms Warner reports is consistent with there being only two generations recognized in the classificatory system.

In sum, it seems likely that the classificatory kinship system of the Murngin is one with bilateral first-cross-cousin marriage with only two classificatory generations distinguished in each of the two lines of descent. A man can legitimately marry any woman in his own generation in the opposite moiety. This is the behavioral implication of the Murngin's own explicit, though atrophied, system of eight named subsections. At one point Warner himself says, "Theoretically an individual can marry into any one of the clans in the opposite moiety" (p. 16). The system of kinship terms predicated on matrilateral marriage used by the Murngin is only a rudimentary classificatory system. It does not delimit categories of eligible spouses, but rather is used in a flexible and necessarily inconsistent way to record the important historical connections through marriage of some hordes to ego's horde. Although it is logically inevitable that the application of these kin terms will give rise to inconsistencies in usage among sets of egos, terms are presumably chosen in such a way as to minimize inconsistencies in the terms used between pairs of men in frequent interaction.

It has not been easy to use Warner's book. Ambiguities and apparent inconsistencies are common. Few systematic hard data are reported, relative to the length of the book: one must be content largely with anecdotes and with Warner's interpretations. The sheer complexity of the Murngin kinship patterns and the size of the population studied may be partly responsible. Certainly it is not meet for one who has done no field work whatever to criticize data gathered in years of field work, presumably often uncomfortable and discouraging and conducted in bizarre languages. Another difficulty may have been the intellectual cross-pressures on Warner, which are symbolized by the contrast between the dedication to Radcliffe-Brown and the curiously worded introduction by Lowie. Other characteristics of the book are less easily explained. Repeatedly Warner tells us that certain crucial cases of marriage, etc., are well verified because they are "recorded," but he never explains what this means. On p. 5 he makes a very powerful statement with no evidence at all: "The blood feud is forever present and tends to kill a sufficient number of young men to allow the system of polygamy to function." When Warner does give specific numerical data they sometimes have an arbitrary ring to them: thus in classifying battles in which men were killed Warner says that there were 15 of one kind, 10 of a second, 5 of a third, and 5 of a fourth kind (p. 159), for a neat total of 35.

3.5. The Purums

"The Purums extensively practice cross-cousin marriage of one type, namely, with the mother's brother's daughter, the other type, i.e., with the father's sister's daughter being strictly tabooed. . . . Thus, out of a total of 85 unions recorded in 1936 in the three villages of the Purums, 63 . . . happened to be brought about by union with the mother's brother's daughters, and in eleven . . . cases the bride was taken from the sib of the mother's brother." It seems reasonable to hope to find a consistent classificatory kinship system of Type II (matrilateral first-cross-cousin marriage) among this hill tribe of the Indo-Burma border on the strength of this quotation from p. 241 of Tarakchandra Das' monograph, *The Purums: An Old Kuki Tribe of Manipur*, published in 1945 by the University of Calcutta. Five distinct sets of detailed data on marriage included by Das enable one to analyze the system in detail for once. Mr. Das is so modest as to say his is "neither an exhaustive nor an intensive study" (p. vii) and it is true that his field procedures are often unclear and his sets of data often are inconsistent. There is little of value in the brief accounts of the Purum in earlier published works. According to the Census of India of 1931 (Vol. III, Assam, Part II, Tables, p. 262), the Purums numbered 145 men and 158 women, all practicing their ancestral tribal religion.

"The data on which [the monograph] is based were collected in course of four excursions into the interior of Manipur Hills from 1931 to 1936. The period of our stay in this area did not altogether run beyond four or five months on four different occasions" (p. 1). Das and other faculty and students in anthropology at the University of Calcutta apparently studied a number of tribes in this area in part as a program of field training. The Purums (and their neighbors) regard themselves as a separate tribe, and they have their own dialect or language, their own territory, and are in fact an endogamous unit, but they feel it legitimate to marry into one nearby tribe, the Chawte, and have been influenced heavily by social, religious, political, and economic customs of the many distinct tribes in their region. Das' party lived in government Rest Houses a few miles from the Purum. Das writes in English but spoke Hindi to his three State interpreters, two of them from Old Kuki tribes, who in turn used Meithei, the lingua franca of the hills understood by most of the Purums.

Eight genealogies, which contain both male and female lines of descent and also name spouses and which overlap partially, constitute Appendix I: who supplied and confirmed which tables is not stated. Appendix II contains 177 statements of how one named individual in the last five genealogies addressed another named individual: Chauba shown in Genealogy IV was the sole informant (p. 141), but he was ego or the person addressed in only twenty of the statements. A list of the types of blood relatives corresponding to each of 26 Purum terms of relationship was derived from the two appendices and shown as Table XII (pp. 147–152); I found numerous inconsistencies and omissions in the derivation. This list was confirmed at least in part by questioning of the man Chongshel, shown in Genealogy I, but not mentioned in Appendix II. Das is not sure which of the Purum terms are terms of address, which terms of reference, which are both, and which are general terms of respect or liking rather than terms of kinship relation. It is also not clear which of the suffixes and prefixes in the kinship terms are essential to their meaning.

Often relatives in three different generations are assigned the same term in Table XII: e.g., Ka-upa refers to MF, MB, and MBS. "Neighboring" lines of descent often contain the same term: e.g., Ka-upa also refers to FF and FFF. Collateral lines are sometimes merged in the terminology, e.g., Ka-upa also refers to FFB, but there are distinct terms for F and FB as well as for M and MZ. Not only does ego distinguish between elder and younger siblings but also he assigns different terms to some relatives several "steps" away according to whether the relationship is through say the elder or the younger brother of his father. There is no clearly consistent relation between the grouping of relatives by kin terms applied by male ego and the grouping according to the kin terms applied by female ego: note that apparently no female informants were used. In a small inbred society there are often a number of different ways of tracing the relation between two individuals. Even in Das' partial data many such ambiguities appear, and they may be responsible for anomalies in his list of relatives by kin terms.

Das claims that the grouping of relatives by kin terms is consistent with a system of marriage with the mother's brother's daughter. Some of the 21 equations he cites (pp. 143–44) indicate no more than that two brothers may tend to marry two sisters. As he points out, other equations expected for a matrilateral system are either not satisfied or the data did not reach far enough to test them. The decisive point, however, is that there are in Das' list many other equations of relatives through the same kin term which are not consistent with matrilateral marriage or indeed any consistent structure of prescriptive marriage in a classificatory kinship system. It is only by heavy pruning and editing of Das' original data or of his Table XII that one can produce a chart of kin terms which resembles Warner's chart for the Murngin shown earlier in having ZH and successor lines distinct from WB and successor lines and both distinct from ego's line.

Perhaps the system of terms of relationship used by Purum toward their known relatives is too complex and ambiguous to be an integral part of any consistent classificatory structure for marriage and descent. A central question for any closed structure in a small society is how to place with respect to ego all the people whose exact relation to him he does not know or care to trace. Among the Kariera and Arunta it was seen that patrilineal local groups were folded into a few descent lines such that every individual was assimilated to one of a relatively few relationships with respect to any ego. A different and simpler set of terms than those in Table XII are used by a Purum to designate persons related to him only through convention formulated in terms of their patrilineal sibs.

"... the Purums are divided into five sibs, namely, Marrim, Makan, Kheyang, Thao, and Parpa. . . . The Purum sib was not only an exogamous unit but it was something more. Purum boys and girls could marry only in one or more selected sibs. Such unions between the different sibs were fixed by traditional customs. Besides this there was another custom by which the boys and girls of any one of these sibs might not marry into the same sib. . . . Among the Purums unrelated persons of both sexes address one another by a number of definitely fixed terms of address on the basis of marital relationship subsisting between different sibs. . . . (this is often relaxed and persons related are also addressed with these terms)" (pp. 121, 123, 125). Male ego addresses all older women in his father's sib by one term, all older women in the group of sibs from which he and his father and other sib mates get wives by another term, and applies a third term to all older women in the group of sibs to which his Z, FZ, etc., go in marriage. Ego addresses younger persons by their personal names. Since generations are not distinguished, one can represent these sib terms of address by arrows between circles representing sibs as in Fig. 3.9, which represents the data in Table V, p. 127, of Das. The three subsequent tables in Das complete for the other sex combinations his report of "a more or less complete collection of such terms of address used by men and women of each sib in relation to the members of their own sib as well as of every other sib" (p. 126).

Men of the sib at the head of a dotted arrow in Fig. 3.9 call women in the sib at the arrow's foot by the term appropriate to ZH sib, while men at the foot of a solid arrow call women at the head by the term for sibs containing W. In eight of the ten pairings of sibs a solid arrow parallels the dotted arrow; so the men in the two sibs agree on the relation between them. However, in each of the pairs Kheyang-Parpa and Kheyang-Marrim men of either sib call women of the other sib by the term for ZH sibs, which would seem to imply an exchange of sisters between sibs, contrary to the norm. The figure representing terms applied by men to men would be identical with Fig. 3.9 with two exceptions: (1) Kheyang and Marrim people still apply the same

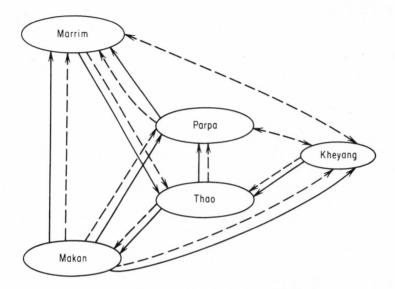

Fig. 3.9. Traditional marriage relations among five named sibs implied by terms of address used by men of one sib towards women of another. Men of the sib at the head of a dotted arrow call women in the sib at the base by the term appropriate for ZH sib. Men at the foot of a solid arrow call women at the head by the term appropriate to sibs containing W, M, etc.

term to each other but the term is that for W sibs not for ZH sibs; (2) the other anomaly in Fig. 3.9 is removed because Kheyang men apply the term for men of WB sibs to Parpa men. Both anomalies in Fig. 3.9 disappear in the table for terms women apply to men—Parpa and Marrim men are addressed as belonging to the sibs of Kheyang men's wives—but a new one appears in that Parpa and Makan women each address the men of the other sib as if they were of their husband's sibs—that is, as if women were exchanged between Parpa and Makan.

Persons in each sib regard every other sib as being a legitimate source either of wives or of husbands but not of both. Instead of the cycle necessary for a consistent unilateral marriage structure one has the complex structure of Fig. 3.9 in which two sibs are equivalent for marriage purposes in the eyes of some other sib but not in the eyes of themselves or of still another sib. Not only is the structure inconsistent by the logic for ideal types of classificatory kinship systems, but also in each set of terms of address there is at least one reciprocal usage which implies that wives can be exchanged bilaterally between a pair of sibs. Except for the latter reciprocal usages the marital relations between sibs inferred from terms of address agree with those submitted by the informant Chauba.

Das gives the sib as well as the name of most persons in the eight genealogical tables. In Fig. 3.10 are shown graphically the results of tabulating 84 distinct married couples by sibs of the spouses. At the base of each arrow is the number of men from that sib who marry women in the sib at the head. (On pp. 133–137 Das tabulates what appear to be 93 marriages from the genealogies, but his presentation is confusing and in any case there is no difference in pattern between his tabulation and mine. This is discussed further below.) All arrows (dotted and/or solid) in Fig. 3.9 are duplicated in this new sociogram with two exceptions: in the genealogies there was no marriage of a Parpa man to a Kheyang woman or of a Makan man to a Parpa woman. However three pairs of sibs which have exchanged wives according to the genealogies were linked only in one direction by arrows in the earlier figure.

Is there really a meaningful pattern in marriages between sibs? Thirteen of the twenty possible arrowheads among five sibs are found in Fig. 3.10, although four represent only 1 or 2 of the total of 84 marriages. Perhaps a change in pattern over the past few generations explains the profusion in connections or perhaps the pattern varies from one village to another. Fortunately, for once there are rich data provided, with which the reader of Das can analyze for himself these and other possibilities.

Sixty men came to Das' camp for a series of very detailed physical measurements. Das reports not only these, but also in Table XIII (p. 38 foldout) he lists for each of the men name, age; sibs of self, mother, and wife; villages of birth and of present residence of self and wife (if any), as well as numbers of brothers, sisters, sons, daughters, and wives both living and dead. Presumably

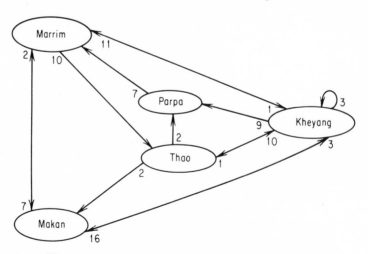

Fig. 3.10. Eighty-four marriages tabulated by sib of each spouse, from genealogy tables, Appendix I of Das, *op. cit.* At the base of each arrow is the number of men of that sib who married women of the sib at the head.

such detailed information must have come from each man himself rather than from some general informant. None of the 60 men had married more than once. None of the names of men in Genealogy I appear in this list of 60 men, and only 5 of the 36 names of men (married and unmarried) in Genealogy IV (in 4 of 5 cases the sib of self is the same and in 3 cases the sib of wife is the same in genealogy as in list). Many men in the genealogies were dead or were small children, but even so the small amount of overlap with the list of 60 seems surprising; the genealogies and the list of 60 men were collected at different times and places and from different people and it may be that variability in pronunciation and spelling of names conceal some of the true overlap.

Of the 60 men 13 are age 20 (but the ages are approximate so these thirteen probably include boys in their late teens), 24 are age 21–29 inclusive, 13 are 30–39, 4 are 40–49, and 6 are 50–60 inclusive. Six of the 60 men are unmarried, all under age 30. The median age of marriage for men seems to be over 20 (p. 240) and the median age of having sons is probably around 30; so probably none of the fathers of the 23 men age 30 or older are included in the list of 60 men. By definition father and child are of the same sib. In Fig. 3.11 the pattern of marriages between sibs contracted by the 31 husbands under age 30 in 1936 is compared with the pattern for the entirely distinct generation of the 23 fathers of men age 30 or more in 1936. Each pattern is a complex structure: there is no evidence for either degeneration away from or evolution toward a clear unilateral marriage structure. The patterns are rather similar,

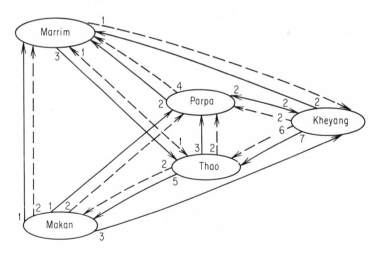

Fig. 3.11. Marriages between sibs in two generations. At the base of each solid arrow is the number of men in that sib under 30 in 1936 who married women of the sib at the arrowhead. At the base of each dotted arrow is the number of men in that sib, fathers of men 30 or over in 1936, who married women of the sib at the arrowhead.

although of course the numbers of marriages are small: eight of the ten dotted arrows (counting a reciprocal arrow as two) match eight of the eleven solid arrows, where among five sibs twenty arrows are logically possible.

Khulen is the largest (40 houses in 1936) of the Purum villages, the others being Tampak (29 houses), Chumbang (12 or 13 houses), and Changninglong (8 or 9 houses). All five sibs are represented among men born in Khulen, and similarly for Tampak. Khulen, the oldest, is the village of birth for both parents of each of the 60 men in Das' Table XIII (p. 38). Thirty of these 60 men not only were born in Khulen but also married women born in Khulen, and probably they all grew up in Khulen. One might expect a simple pattern of marriage, closer to the cyclic structure of a consistent classificatory kinship model, among localized segments of the five sibs, especially for just boys and girls who married after growing up in one village. Figure 3.12 does not support this expectation.

Apparently any move to a new village is normally made by men just after their marriage at the time of setting up their new home, if any (pp. 247, 250). Of the 37 married men from Das' list born in Khulen, 9 resided in Tampak in 1936, and 3 in Changninglong or elsewhere (all married men born in Tampak or Changninglong resided in their village of birth in 1936). One might think a husband would move primarily to join the village of his wife, but of the 9 Khulen-born men who resided in Tampak, 4 had married girls born in Khulen, and it may be that the 5 who married girls born in Tampak were residing there only to finish the three years of bride-work (p. 242) since Das does not say whether he counts betrothal as marriage or exactly what residence means.

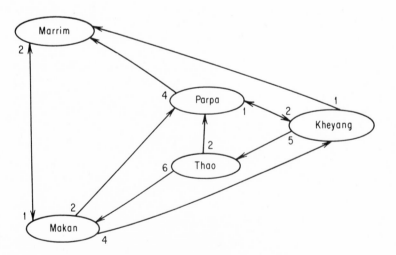

Fig. 3.12. Marriages of 30 couples born in Khulen village. At the base of each arrow is the number of men of that sib who marry women of the sib at the arrowhead.

Twenty-eight of the 54 husbands in Das' Table XIII had married women from the sib where their father had found their mother. It might be thought that these marriages would be more regular—that is, conform more closely to any simple normative structure of marriages among sibs—but Fig. 3.13 scotches this thought. Also there is no more tendency for men to marry into their mothers' sib when they marry local girls than otherwise: in 22 of 43 marriages of boys and girls born in the same village the boy marries a girl from his mother's sib and in 6 of 11 marriages between villages the same is true.

The fifth and last major set of data on marriage in Das is a tabulation of 128 marriages from a village census (Column b, Table X, pp. 133–137). In the upper left corner of each cell in Table 3.2 is the number of the 128 marriages contracted by men from the sib named in that row with women of the sib named in that column. For comparison, in the upper right corner is the number of such marriages among the 84 couples in the genealogies (Fig. 3.10 above), and in the lower left corner is the number among the 54 marriages of men whom Das measured physically. (See Figs. 3.11, 3.12, 3.13.) In addition, in the lower right corner of a cell there is a check mark if such marriages are implied by any one or more of the four sets of terms of address between sibs. (See Fig. 3.9 above.)

Das never states who is included in the village census, but presumably many of these 128 marriages also appear in the genealogies and/or in the 54 marriages of Table XIII in Das. However no one of the three sets contains all the marriages in either of the other two: (a) 128 is bigger than 84 or 54; (b) there are 13 Kheyang ⟶ Thao marriages among the 54 but only 9 among the

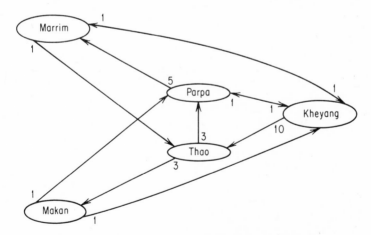

Fig. 3.13. Twenty-eight marriages where the wife is from the sib of her husband's mother. At the base of each arrow is the number of men from that sib who marry into the sib of their mothers at the head of the arrow.

128 and 10 among the 84; (c) there are 11 Marrim ⟶ Kheyang marriages among the 84 but only 6 among the 128 and 1 among the 54.

One extreme way to combine various sets of data is to say marriage of men in one sib to women of another is allowed if there is any evidence for it in any of the sets. Of the 20 off-diagonal cells in Table 3.2 only four have no entries, and one of these (Thao ⟶ Marrim) would have an entry if the data on fathers of the 54 men of Das' Table XIII were included. (See Fig. 3.11 above.) From this extreme point of view, then, practically all marriages between sibs are allowed, and certainly there is no consistent classificatory structure based on matrilateral marriage.

Another extreme way to combine sets of data is to require that each set separately provide evidence for marriage of men of one sib to women of another sib before one says that such a marriage is proper. Like the other

Table 3.2. Classification of three sets* of Purum marriages by sib of husband and sib of wife.

Sib of husband \ Sib of wife	Marrim	Makan	Parpa	Thao	Kheyang	Totals
Marrim	.. .. ..	5 2 1	.. .. ..	10 10 3 √	6 11 1 √	21 23 5
Makan	5 7 2 √	.. .. ..	2 .. 2 √	.. .. ..	20 16 5 √	27 23 9
Parpa	17 7 5 √	.. .. .. √	.. .. ..	.. .. ..	8 .. 3 √	25 7 8
Thao	.. .. ..	16 2 8 √	10 2 5 √	.. .. ..	.. 1 ..	26 5 13
Kheyang	6 1 3 √	2 3 ..	11 9 3 √	9 10 13 √	1 3 ..	29 26 19 ..
Totals	28 15 10	23 7 9	23 11 10	19 20 16	35 31 9	128 84 54

* Key:

A	B
C	

In each cell:
  (A)   number A is of the set of 128 marriages from village census (Das, Table X, columns b, pp. 133–137).
  (B)   number B is of the set of 84 marriages tabulated from the eight genealogy tables (Das, Appendix I).
  (C)   number C is of the set of 54 marriages of men measured physically (Das, Table XIII, p. 38 foldout).

A check appears in the lower right corner if such marriages can be inferred from any term in the four sets of terms of address between sibs (Das, Tables V–VIII, pp. 125–130).

extreme combination this is very sensitive to which sets of data are combined. Since terms of address between sibs would seem to have an inherent normative quality, it is appropriate to treat each set of terms for one sex of one sib addressing one sex of another sib as a separate set. Figure 3.14 shows just those marriage relations among the five sibs implied by all four sets of terms of address. It seems reasonable, although arbitrary, to use just the three total sets of actual marriages between sibs tabulated in Table 3.2 as the other separate sets, since there are rather few marriages reported in the various subsets graphed separately in earlier figures. Each of the seven arrows in Fig. 3.14 also corresponds to one or more marriages in each of these three total sets of marriages. (Also each arrow is justified by one or more marriages among just the 31 husbands less than 30 in Das, Table XIII, p. 38, and among the 54 fathers of all husbands in that table, although one arrow is not justified by marriages among just the 28 out of the total of 54 husbands who marry into their mother's sib and another arrow is not justified by marriages of just the 30 out of 54 husbands who together with their wives are born in Khulen village.)

In short, Fig. 3.14 specifies those seven marriage relations between sibs supported by practically all the separate kinds of data on marriage which one can cull from Das' monograph. With this figure for the first time a consistent structure of relations emerges, a matrilateral structure appropriate to a classificatory kinship system in which generations are not distinguished. Specifically, by the logic of a consistent classificatory system, if Fig. 3.14 shows the proper marriages among the five groupings of local patrilineal descent groups called sibs, the men in Kheyang and Marrim should be classificatory brothers and similarly for Makan and Parpa sibs. In other words,

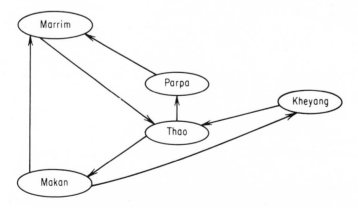

Fig. 3.14. The seven marriage relations between sibs implied by all four sets of terms of address between sibs (and supported by the three total sets of recorded marriages—see text). Each arrow runs from one sib to the sib containing women who are correct wives for men in the first sib.

Kheyang and Marrim sibs should be "folded into" one descent line (here a single node) of a matrilateral classificatory kinship system which marries into Thao, the second descent line, which in turn marries into the third line of Makan and Parpa, which complete the cycle by marrying into the Kheyang plus Marrim line.

Figure 3.15 represents this simple ring of three descent "lines" which might possibly be the normative structure underlying the observed Purum kinship system in some sense. The evidence is certainly weak; in particular the terms of relation used between individual relatives, the first of the five major sets of data, do not form a closed or consistent classificatory system. At the bottom of Fig. 3.15 are listed the fractions of the three total sets of recorded marriages which follow those eight arrows between pairs of sibs which are consistent with the ideal model of a cycle among the three groups of sibs. (The additional consistent arrow is Parpa $\longrightarrow$ Kheyang.) The lowest fraction is 0.64, for the marriages from genealogies: it is hard to see how one can decide whether to say "only 0.64" or to exult and say "0.64!!"

If one breaks down the set of 54 marriages in various ways one finds that the fractions consistent with the ideal model are

> 0.77   for the 30 marriages of couples born in Khulen village,
>
> 0.85   for the 28 marriages of men into the sib of their mother,
>
> 0.84   for the 31 marriages of men under 30,

as compared with 0.81 for the total set; so the extent of agreement with the ideal model does not vary appreciably from one kind of subset to another. Also in an earlier generation the fraction was about the same: 0.74 of the 23 marriages by fathers of husbands over 30 are in conformity with the model.

There is additional evidence to back up the implicit assumption above that the sib is the basic category in the Purums' kinship system. They have a generic name for sib (Sageii—p. 320, Glossary, and p. 117) borrowed from the lingua franca of Meithei, as well as the five individual names. In various origin myths the origin of some or all of the five sibs are explained in terms of patrilineal descent from mythical progenitors (pp. 108–110). Each sib has a headman or pipa who is recognized as a genealogical head and is succeeded in office by his son or younger brother (pp. 121, 139–40). Every pipa has special duties in the worship of a god who is both the sib and the household god among all the Purums (pp. 278–279). In principle, members of the sib in a village share equally the inheritance from a male sib member who dies without leaving anyone in the male line of the family (p. 139). The two oldest male members of a girl's sib come next in line after her parents in the receiving of honorary presents of food at her wedding, and other taboos and customs at the wedding are defined in terms of sib membership (pp. 245–246). Male ego's privileged

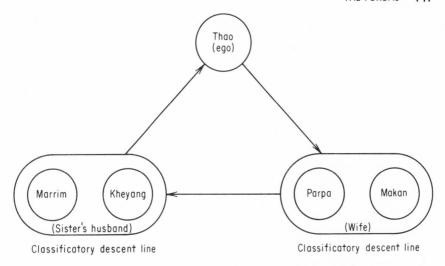

Fig. 3.15. Consistent matrilateral kinship structure
(W³ = I, C = I) corresponding to previous Figure
which may represent underlying norms of the Purums.*
Ovals enclose sibs equivalent to each other ("folded
into" the same line of descent, classificatory brothers).

familiarity of telling sexual jokes is extended from his MBD to the unmarried
girls of his MB sib (p. 153). Each sib has a separate area in the burial ground
(p. 253—the wife is buried beside her husband although in all other respects
apparently she is considered to remain a member of her sib of birth, that of
her father).

Exogamy is part of the normal definition of a sib by anthropologists. In
the axiomatic definition of consistent closed structures of marriage and descent
based on classificatory kinship in Chapter 2 only exogamy for generations
(clans) within a line of descent was assumed, but among the Purums generations are not kept distinct; so if any of these ideal models is to fit the Purums
each constituent unit must be one or more collections of people acknowledging
common descent who never should or do marry among themselves. The
Purums have an explicit rule against sib endogamy, but Das cites one case of a
father of Kheyang sib marrying another woman in Kheyang sib of a different
lineage and his two sons following suit (pp. 122–123). Since there was no
evidence of disapproval of these marriages Das concludes that the sib is
slowly disintegrating into constituent lineages or subsibs within each of which
exogamy is still a rigid norm.

* The fractions of observed marriages consistent with this structure in various sets of
data in Table 3.2 are:

        0.74   of the 128 marriages in census,
        0.64   of the 84 marriages in genealogies,
        0.81   of the 54 marriages of men measured physically.

Named subsibs or lineages exist in four of the sibs although there is no generic name for subsib (pp. 118–119). The pipa of each of these four sibs is also the pipa of its principal subsib (p. 139), which is numbered 1 below. Only for the subsibs starred below is Das able to give the name of their pipas; all these pipas reside in Khulen village (p. 120). Thao-kung and Thao-run lineages have the same pipa. Unfortunately, tabulation by subsib is complete only for the set of 128 marriages in the village census.

In Table 3.3 is shown the cross-classification by subsib of the 128 marriages already tabulated by sib in Table 3.2. Subsibs named by Das for which no marriages or headmen are reported have been omitted; the numbering of subsibs is as in Das, except for the two Impi lineages which he chooses to largely ignore. In Das' Table X the cross-tabulation of these 128 marriages is listed once according to the subsib of husband and again according to the subsib of wife: the two listings agree except that the two Impi lineages and the three Parpa → Julhung marriages are omitted in the listing by wife while four instead of three Parpa → Rimphunchong marriages are listed there.

Only one pair of subsibs (note Parpa is counted a sib) have exchanged wives according to Table 3.3: Julhung and Pilling. In only 3 of the 84 marriages by sib in Das' published genealogies reported in Table 3.2 are the subsibs of both husband and wife specified. However, of the 93 marriages tabulated by Das (in Table X, pp. 133–137) from genealogies apparently more detailed than the ones he published, 22 are reported by subsib both of husband and of wife. Fifteen of the 22 can be entered in 6 cells of Table 3.3 which are already occupied, but 7 marriages are in 5 types (cells) which do not occur in Table 3.3 for the 128 marriages from village census. Only 2 of the 7 are reported both in the list by subsib of husband and the list by subsib of wife although these lists should be merely restatements of one another. If just these 2 marriages (of 2 types) are added to Table 3.3, then one additional exchange of wives between a pair of subsibs appears, for Julhung ↔ Rangshai; if all 7 (or for that matter all 22) genealogy marriages are added to Table 3.3 then a third exchange of wives also appears: Kankung ↔ Aihung.

Even when subsibs instead of sibs are considered the exogamous kin groups, the 128 marriages from the village census do not conform to a consistent classificatory kinship system, matrilateral or any other. Quite aside from the cases above where one or more wives are given by one subsib to another which obtains one or more wives from the first, there are numerous inconsistencies in the marriage pattern among trios of subsibs. For example, Julhung and Rimkung subsibs both have taken wives from Thao-kung, in whose eyes they are therefore brothers by classificatory logic, and yet Julhung takes wives from Rimkung. To take a converse example, Kankung and Thao-kung both furnish wives to Aihung lineage and yet Kankung supplies wives to Thao-kung.

One could extract a pattern of marriage among subsibs which reduces to a consistent classificatory structure and which contains most of the recorded

Table 3.3. Marriages between subsibs from village census.†

Subsib of husband	Subsib of wife	Marrim 1	Marrim 2	Marrim 3	Marrim 4	Makan 1	Makan 2	Makan 3	Parpa	Thao 1	Thao 2	Thao 4	Kheyang 1	Kheyang 2	Kheyang 3	Total
Marrim	1. Rimphunchong*	..				4							3			7
	2. Rimkung*		..							2	4					6
	3. Rim-ke-lek			..						4						4
	4. Pilling*				..	1							2	1		4
Makan	1. Kankung*		5			..			2				18			25
	2. Makan-te*						..						2			2
	3. Makan-Impi							..								0
Parpa		3	4		10				..				3	3	2	25
Thao	1. Thao-kung*					2			6	..	..					8
	2. Thao-run*					10		2	4	..						16
	4. Rangshai*					2						..				2
Kheyang	1. Julhung*		2		2				10	2		4	..	1		21
	2. Aihung		2			2			1	3			..	..		8
	3. Kheyang-Impi													..	..	0
		3	13	0	12	21	0	2	23	11	4	4	28	5	2	128

* Only starred subsibs have named headmen. The headman of a sib is also the headman of the principal lineage, which is given the number 1. Subsibs 1 and 2 of Thao have the same headman.

† The same 128 marriages are cross-classified by sib only in the upper left-hand corners of cells in Table 3.2.

marriages. Many such patterns could be found, however, and there are not enough data to justify the choice of a particular pattern through a combination of independent evidence, as was the case in the derivation of Fig. 3.15 for sibs. There is nothing corresponding to the terms of address between sibs to provide a guide to any norms governing marriages between subsibs. Nor can one test whether the observed patterns of marriages among subsibs are the same for couples of different age groups and villages. There are $14 \times 13 = 182$ possible types of marriage between subsibs, and in the absence of explicit norms it does not seem reasonable to rule out any of these types as improper when only 128 marriages have been observed. After all, many of the 35 types of marriage between subsibs actually found in the set of 128 marriages represent only one or two recorded cases. Das really presents very little evidence to back up his theory that the propriety of marriages was more and more being considered in terms of subsibs rather than sibs by the Purums, and in any case the pattern of marriages between subsibs seems no more consistent or clear than the pattern of marriages between sibs.

One is tempted to ignore the inconsistent triangles of marriages among trios of descent groups, whether sibs or subsibs, and instead to show how the observed structure of marriages can be decomposed into closed cycles of three or more links. One can assign recorded marriages to a given cycle such that each group passes on to the next the same number of wives that it received from the preceding group in the cycle. By a judicious choice of decomposition almost any set of recorded marriages can be allocated among a set of cycles in this way. Such a procedure is quite arbitrary. There is no evidence that Purums conceive of their system in such terms. Marriages of different men in the same group (whether sib or subsib) would often be assigned to different cycles in such a decomposition, and there is no evidence that there are distinctions drawn between men in the subsib according to what cycle they are conceived to be members of.

All Purums expect to marry and apparently practically all do marry. If a man cannot find a woman in the group or groups into which it is customary for his group to marry, whether the custom is formulated in terms of sibs or of subsibs, he can be expected to turn elsewhere. The smaller the constituent groups, the more likely are imbalances in the numbers of men and women eligible to marry strictly according to custom. The row marginals in Table 3.2 for marriages between sibs are more nearly equal to each other and to the column marginals than in Table 3.3. Even in Table 3.2, however, it seems clear that not all marriages can conform to any one customary pattern among sibs indefinitely. Figure 3.11 is more directly relevant, since the numbers of marriages shown there (solid arrows) are all for young men near enough the same age to marry most of the young women involved; naturally one would really need a complete census by ten-year age groups of all Purum marriages to develop a reliable picture of imbalances in eligible spouses and their variation over time. Many Australian kinship systems distinguish between generations, and on this score are likely to be more plagued by such imbalances than tribes like the Purums, but on the other hand the former practice polygamy and accept a much wider range of age differences between spouses than do the Purums and on these grounds can show more flexibility in adapting to imbalances without departing from the marriage norms.

There are many puzzling inconsistencies in Das' book. His references to the villages from which various data come are often contradictory. In the quote with which this account began Das claims that 63 of 85 marriages were with "the mother's brother's daughter." It is hard to be sure which set of recorded marriages he refers to there, but in any case this claim does not sit well with the fact that only 28 of the 54 marriages of living men Das recorded in Table XIII (p. 38) are even into the same sib as the husband's mother, much less to male ego's own mother's brother's daughter. Das further claimed that all 42 marriages (of the total set of 85) contracted by couples then residing in Khulen were marriages of male ego to mother's brother's daughter (p. 241); yet from the list of 54 couples in Das' Table XIII in only 9 out of the 25 couples then residing in Khulen had the husband even married into the sib of his mother. Earlier it was seen that Das' material on terms of relationship was unreliable and confused; so perhaps he gave a narrower construction (p. 150) than was warranted to the term ka-nau-nu. Also Das' account of the flexible and rather voluntaristic procedures by which a marriage is formed (p. 240) does not seem compatible with his description of marriage as quite rigidly determined by genealogical relation.

In this book, *prescriptive marriage* means marriage in a kinship system which satisfies the eight axioms of Chapter 2. *Matrilateral marriage system* is the shorthand name for such a system in which the operator relations $WC = CW$ and $W^2 \neq I$ hold. Neither the recorded marriages nor the kinship terminology of the Purums are consistent with either these axioms or these relations, no matter what particular matrilateral model is considered. Yet there is some correspondence between Purum reality and the simple matrilateral model of Fig. 3.15.

3.6. Models and Data

"My surest evidence came, however, from the remarkably lucid exposition of the class-system by the natives themselves. Even without relationship systems and pedigrees, this exposition would suffice to establish the existence and structure of the matrimonial class organization in Ambryn" (an island of the New Hebrides). A. Bernhard Deacon included these comments in his description of a kinship system which appears to conform to Fig. 2.24(b) above ["The Regulation of Marriage in Ambryn," *Journal of the Royal Anthropological Institute*, **57** (1927), 238]. Similar comments can be found in some field reports on Australian tribes. The more clearly a tribe, or at least some of its senior men, visualizes its kinship relations in terms of the functioning of a closed and consistent system, the easier the task of the analyst.

Even where the tribe has an explicit "official" kinship system, however, it does not follow that one knows the norms applied to actual behavior of individuals, much less the extent to which behavior conforms to norms. A tribe may consciously adopt a new total kinship system in principle, but yet not be able to conceive and carry out necessary modifications of kinship relations among concrete individuals, which continue to be subject in part to the previous norms. [See, for example, W. E. H. Stanner, "Murinbata Kinship and Totemism," *Oceania*, 7 (1936), 186–216, esp. 199 ff.] More generally, a tribe may try to follow simultaneously a number of somewhat inconsistent marriage rules and concomitant kinship systems so that there is much scope for individual manipulation of norms. [See, for example, A. P. Elkin, R. M. Berndt, and C. H. Berndt, "Social Organization of Arnhem Land: I. Western Arnhem Land," *Oceania*, **21** (1951), 253–301, esp. 261, 275, 281, in which account one of the ideal kinship systems is that in Fig. 2.12 above.] As has already been shown (Sec. 3.3) the ideal kinship system approximated in actual behavior and specific norms may be more complex than that recognized by the tribe's members: the structure can be identified only by a successive approximation procedure since a particular clan can be defined only by its position in the whole structure of clans treated as a system.

A mass of data—on perceived norms, local horde membership, descent groups, kinship terms used for one another by at least a large fraction of tribe members, the composition of explicit kin divisions like moieties and sections, together with extensive records of marriages containing all such information for both spouses—is necessary to establish reliably any system or fragments of systems to which various aspects of kinship behavior in a tribe may conform in fact or in principle. Nothing like this quantity of data is presented in existing accounts of a tribe's kinship behavior. A substantial fraction of the systematic data in an observer's field notes is presumably omitted from his printed accounts because of publishing costs, and it might be possible to retrieve such information for some tribes in usable form. Some journals like *Oceania* permit lengthy detailed accounts continued through several volumes, and much can be done to piece together such material so as to produce analyses at least as detailed as the four in this chapter.

Anthropologists in general have not been intent on gathering the volume of systematic data required for full analyses of kinship systems of individual tribes. The definition of a tribe both vis-à-vis its neighbors and in terms of time span is arbitrary to a considerable extent for Australia and other large land areas. Many anthropologists think of their task primarily as one of mapping roughly the incidence of various principles of kinship organization over broad areas. (See, for example, the introduction to the first volume of *Oceania* written by its editor, A. P. Elkin.) They then tease out from scattered clues ideas as to how and why one principle is modified or replaced over time or over a range in space. To treat a "tribe" as a separate unit with a closed system of kinship behavior *is* somewhat artificial, but it has the advantage of requiring more precise and exhaustive data from the field worker. Plausible hypotheses about the evolution of kinship principles are valuable—for example, A. P. Elkin's argument that unilateral cross-cousin marriage can be an intermediate step between simple Kariera and more complex bilateral marriage systems in Australia [*Oceania*, 2 (1931–32), 296–337, esp. 302, 318–320] —but even repeated examples of trends in kinship organization over time and space cannot substantiate such hypotheses unless exhaustive data are available for some cases. The field anthropologist has read much of the literature and necessarily has preconceptions about each tribe he studies—why did he choose it?—so that one must be sceptical about superficial reports on an arc of territory which fit into an immediately plausible pattern. This is especially true since conclusions about a particular tribe often are explicitly based partly on inferences from how neighboring tribes are reputed to behave, with little specific objective data in support. (See, for example, A. R. Radcliffe-Brown's survey of interpretation of Australian systems in *Oceania*, Monograph No. 1; also see U. McConnel's extended series of articles in *Oceania* over a twenty-year span on junior marriage systems among tribes of the Cape York peninsula.) Also, kinship systems are complex and one would expect there to be a very large number of ways in which at least some aspects of each of a number of kinship systems can be fitted together to support a plausible genetic explanation.

Extensive systematic data on one tribe are presented in the distinguished scientific field report by F. G. G. Rose in his *Classification of Kin, Age Structure, and Marriage Amongst the Groote Eylandt Aborigines* (Berlin; Akademie-Verlag, 1960, 571 pp.). Photographs have long been a commonplace in anthropologists' reports, but Rose was apparently the first to systematically compile a set of photographs of (most) members of a tribe and with its aid find out what kinship terms each person applied to each other. Rose presents in extensive tables this (nearly raw) data on terminology plus information on blood relationship, totems, initiation, and inferred age. As A. P. Elkin has pointed out [fn. 18, p. 14, in "The Complexity of Social Organization in Arnhem Land," *Southwestern Journal of Anthropology*, 6 (1950)], there is little in the way of clear models of their own kinship system recognized by these aborigines to guide investigation. Rose largely neglects local group membership, and the tribe has no developed section system, but these rich data should provide a basis for analysis of how classificatory kinship terminology persists and develops when the kinds of consistency postulated in Chapter 1 are not maintained.

Models are as essential as data in achieving satisfactory understanding of kinship ideals and behavior. The literature on unilateral cross-cousin marriage illustrates this need. By no means is the amount of data here embarrassingly large. For example, the Kandyu tribe of Cape York peninsula is cited in monographs as one with patrilateral first-cross-cousin marriage. [See, for example, pp. 56, 101–2 of R. Needham, *Structure and Sentiment* (Chicago: University of Chicago Press, 1960).] Yet the principal field report was based on a single respondent, an old man who was a police tracker and "diffident concerning his own knowledge of the tribal customs" [U. H. McConnel, "Junior Marriage Systems: Comparative Survey," *Oceania*, **21** (1950–51), 109]. As grave as uncertainty about facts, and related to it, is the uncertainty in definitions of unilateral marriage.

Prescriptive unilateral marriage has been differentiated sharply from preferential forms. In the words of Needham:

> The term "prescriptive," on the other hand, has quite different connotations. In this case the emphasis is on the very lack of choice: the category or type of person to be married is precisely determined, and this marriage is obligatory. Among the Batak of Sumatra, for instance, marriage is prescribed with a woman exclusively of the category *born in tulang*, of which one of the genealogical specifications is "mother's brother's daughter." [*Structure and Sentiment* (Chicago: University of Chicago Press, 1960), p. 9.]

This definition is incomplete for the same reason that Radcliffe-Brown's argument in favor of a genealogical interpretation of Australian marriage rules falls flat. (See Sec. 3.1 above.) Unless the definition stipulates a consistent kinship system of the kind we have defined in Chapters 1 and 2 one cannot unambiguously define a category of equivalent positions in the network of kin relations, that is, a clan in our terms. The number of clans must be small relative to the number of people if the marriage system is to be viable, so that a small inbred society must conform to one of the closed models discussed in Chapter 2 if it is to follow a truly prescriptive marriage rule. Otherwise it is logically impossible for there to be public agreement that everyone marries the prescribed category of classificatory relative; e.g., in the Murngin as described by Warner each man may assert he marries his MBD who is not his FZD, but in the eyes of at least some other tribe members the spouse will be a bilateral first cross cousin. If there is not public agreement on an unambiguous category of allowed spouses there can be no clear difference between obligatory or prescriptive and merely preferential marriage rules—unless one wishes to base the distinction on the fervor with which informants insist the rule is obligatory.

It should be evident that unambiguous prescriptive marriage is a limiting case, an ideal type. One should ask not whether a tribe has a prescriptive as opposed to a preferential marriage system, but rather to what extent the tribe conforms to one or to some mixture of ideal types of prescribed marriage systems, either as an isolated unit or as part of an interacting network of tribes. There remains the difficult task of developing a more general framework of analysis within which one can meaningfully and with precision define the extent of conformity. In this book I have succeeded only in deriving the ideal types. Chance mechanisms probably must be included in a more general framework: to provide a basis for measuring mixtures of ideal systems; to allow for individual deviations from any of the recognized norms not corrected by such mechanisms as adoption; and to provide a basis for assessing the demographic stability of a given ideal system or mixture of systems. Once such a framework is developed one can hope to test meaningful theories, presumably of a stochastic nature, of the evolution of classificatory kinship systems.

Additional References

Works not cited above which were very helpful or very stimulating to me are:

W. E. Lawrence, "Alternating Generations in Australia," in G. P. Murdock, ed., *Studies in the Science of Society* (New Haven: Yale University Press, 1937).

E. A. Hammel, "Some Models for the Analysis of Marriage-Section Systems," *Oceania*, **31** (1960), 14–26.

E. R. Leach, "Jinghpaw Kinship Terminology," *Journal of the Royal Anthropological Institute*, **75** (1945), 59–72.

M. Fortes, *The Dynamics of Clanship among the Tallensi* (London: Oxford University Press, 1945).

B. S. Lane, "Varieties of Cross-cousin Marriage and Incest Taboos: Structure and Causality," in G. E. Dole and R. L. Carneiro, eds., *Essays in the Science of Culture* (New York: Thomas Y. Crowell Co., 1960).

B. S. Lane, "Structural Contrasts between Symmetric and Asymmetric Marriage Systems: A Fallacy" (pp. 49–56), and the rejoinder by E. R. Leach (pp. 343–352) in *Southwestern Journal of Anthropology*, **17** (1961).

R. Needham, "A Structural Analysis of Purum Society," *American Anthropologist*, **60** (1958), 75–101.

W. E. H. Stanner, "Aboriginal Modes of Address and Reference in the North-west of the Northern Territory," *Oceania*, **7** (1936–37), 300–315.

On the Algebraic Study of Certain Types of Marriage Laws (Murngin's System)*

ANDRÉ WEIL

In these few pages, written at the request of C. Lévi-Strauss, I propose to show how certain types of marriage laws can be submitted to algebraic calculation and how algebra and the theory of groups of permutations can facilitate study and classification.

In the societies being considered, individuals, males and females, are divided into classes, the class of each one being determined, according to certain rules, by those of his parents; and the marriage rules indicate, according to the respective classes of a man and woman, whether or not they can marry.

In such a society, the total possible marriages can then be divided into a number of distinct types; this number is equal to the number of classes into which the population is divided, if there is a unique formula which, for a man of a given class, indicates from which class he may choose his wife (or, in other terms, the sister of the man into whose class he may marry); if, on the other hand, there are several such formulae, alternating among themselves in a determined manner, then the number of types of possible marriages can be double, triple, etc., the number of classes.

Let n, in any case, equal the number of types of marriage; we arbitrarily

* Part 1 of Chap. 14 (Appendix to Part I) of C. Lévi-Strauss, *Elementary Structures of Kinship* (Paris: Presses Universitaires de France, 1949). Translated by Cynthia White. Published with the kind permission of the Beacon Press.

designate them by n symbols, for example, $M_1, M_2, \ldots, M_n$. We shall consider only the marriage laws satisfying the following conditions:

(A) For each individual, male or female, there is one and only one type of marriage which he (or she) has the right to contract.

(B) For each individual, the type of marriage which he (or she) is capable of contracting depends solely on his sex and the type of marriage of which he (or she) is the issue.

Consequently, the type of marriage possible to a son, issue of a marriage of type M_i (i being one of the number $1, 2, \ldots, n$), is a function of M_i, which we can, following the mathematical notation used in such a case, designate by $f(M_i)$. There will be, similarly for a daughter, a corresponding function, which we shall designate by $g(M_i)$, being ordinarily distinct from the preceding (function). The knowledge of these two functions f and g determines completely, from an abstract point of view, the rules of marriage in the society being studied. These rules can then be represented by a table of three lines of which the first enumerates the types of marriage $M_1, \ldots, M_n$, while the second and third give the respective corresponding values of the two functions f and g.

Let us take a simple case. Let there be a society of four classes, with a generalized exchange of this type:

There are four types of marriage: (M_1) male A, female B; (M_2) male B, female C; (M_3) male C, female D; (M_4) male D, female A. Let us further allow that the children of a mother of class A, B, C, D be respectively of class B, C, D, A. Then our table is the following:

Type of parents' marriage		M_1	M_2	M_3	M_4
Type of son's marriage $f(M_i)$	$= M_3$	M_4	M_1	M_2
Type of daughter's marriage $g(M_i)$	$= M_2$	M_3	M_4	M_1

Moreover, as it would appear from the above case, f and g are the permutations among $M_1, \ldots, M_n$; in other words, in our table, the second line (which gives values of f) and the third (values of g) are, like the first, composed of the symbols $M_1, \ldots, M_n$, simply arranged in a different order from that of the previous line. In fact, if such were not the case, certain types of marriage would disappear as early as the second generation. This already shows that our study springs from the theory of permutations among n elements, a theory which goes back to Lagrange and Galois and which has been carried much further since their time.

Now let us introduce a new condition:

(C)   All males ought to be able to marry the daughter of their mother's brother.

Let us express it algebraically. Consider a brother and sister, issues of a marriage of type M_i; the brother must contract a marriage $f(M_i)$ so that his daughter will contract a marriage $g[f(M_i)]$; the sister must contract a marriage $g(M_i)$ so that her son will contract a marriage $f[g(M_i)]$; the condition (C) is thus expressed by this relation:

$$f[g(M_i)] = g[f(M_i)].$$

This condition is known, in group theory, as the commutativity of permutations f and g. Pairs of commuting permutations can be studied and classified according to known principles. In the language of group theory (which it is scarcely possible, unfortunately, to translate into nontechnical terms without overlong explanations), the group of permutations generated by f and g is an "abelian group" which, having two generators, is necessarily cyclic, or else a direct product of two cyclic groups.

Here a new condition is introduced which we shall express by means of the following definition. We shall say that a society is *reducible* if it is possible to distinguish in it two or several subpopulations of the sort in which there would never be any kinship tie between the individuals of one and the individuals of another. In the contrary case, the society would be called *irreducible*. It is clear that, from the point of view of a purely abstract study of the types of marriage laws, one can limit oneself to the consideration of irreducible societies, since in a reducible society everything takes place as if each subpopulation constituted a distinct society which, in itself, is irreducible. For example, consider a system of limited exchange:

Hence, four types of marriage: (M_1) male A, female B; (M_2) male B, female A; (M_3) male C, female D; (M_4) male D, female C. Let us suppose that all children be of the same class A, B, C, or D as their mother. This society is, evidently, reducible, and composed of two subpopulations, formed, the one of classes A and B, the other of classes C and D. The table of functions f and g for this society is as follows:

	M_1	M_2	M_3	M_4
$f(M_i) =$	M_2	M_1	M_4	M_3
$g(M_i) =$	M_1	M_2	M_3	M_4

To grant that one is dealing with an irreducible society is to grant, in the language of group theory, that the group defined above (abelian group of permutations generated by f and g) is transitive. Such a group, if cyclic, is of extremely simple structure; if it is a direct product of two cyclic groups, the possibilities are more varied and the principles of classification to be employed, more complex; but, in any case, these questions can be treated according to known methods. We shall limit ourselves here to stating the results obtained in the case of a cyclic group. For this, it is necessary to explain the well-known principle of arithmetic modulo n.

Let n be any integer. In calculating "modulo n," we always substitute for any number the remainder after it has been divided by n. For example, the proof by "casting out nines," well known in elementary arithmetic, consists in calculating modulo 9. Similarly, if one is to calculate modulo 10, and one is to add 8 and 7 one writes 5; if one has to multiply 3×4 one writes 2; 2×5, one writes 0, etc. This is written thus: $8 + 7 = 5$ (mod 10); $3 \times 4 = 2$ (mod 10), etc.; it is customary, in all calculations of this type, to replace the sign $=$ by $\equiv$ (which is read "congruent to"). In computing modulo 10, one never writes 10 nor any number larger than 10, so that there are in this arithmetic but 10 numbers, namely, $0, 1, 2, \ldots, 9$.

Let us return, then, to the case of an irreducible society with cyclic group. In such a case it is possible to distinguish a certain number n of classes, and to number them from 0 to $n - 1$ in such a way that a man of class x always marries a woman of class $x + a$ (mod n), and that children of a woman of class x be always of class $x + b$ (mod n), a and b being two fixed numbers, and calculations being made modulo n. For example, in the generalized system of exchange described earlier, one finds $n = 4$, $a = 1$, $b = 1$, as one sees in numbering classes A, B, C, D by 0, 1, 2, 3, respectively.

We shall now go on to show how one can formulate and discuss algebraically a more complex example. Let us postulate a system of eight classes, allowing two formulae for marriage applied alternatively:

Let us further allow that the class of children is determined by that of their mother:

Mother's class	A1	A2	B1	B2	C1	C2	D1	D2
Children's class	C2	C1	D2	D1	A1	A2	B1	B2

Finally, it is necessary, in order to apply our method, that we allow a rule for alternation between formulae (I) and (II) that will satisfy the condition (B) laid down in the beginning. Here, we shall make, for ease of calculation, a more precise hypothesis, which is perhaps uselessly restrictive, but with which we shall content ourselves: it is that the formula for marriage (I) or (II) to which a particular individual must conform depends uniquely upon his sex and upon the formula (I) or (II), according to which his parents married.

There are now sixteen types of marriage, according to the class of the spouses and the formula which is applied. We shall not number them from 1 to 16, but in a manner which better lends itself to calculation. In all of the following, the computations are to be understood as modulo 2; in the arithmetic modulo 2, there are only two numbers 0 and 1; the multiplication table is the following: $0 \times 0 = 0$, $0 \times 1 = 0$, $1 \times 0 = 0$, $1 \times 1 = 1$; the addition table is: $0 + 0 = 0$, $0 + 1 = 1$, $1 + 0 = 1$, $1 + 1 = 0$.

Having stated this, we designate each class by a triple index (a, b, c), each one of these indices a, b, and c being one of the numbers of the arithmetic modulo 2, that is to say 0 or 1, and following these rules:

1. a is 0 if the class is A or B, 1 if it is C or D.
2. b is 0 if the class is A or C, 1 if it is B or D.
3. c is 0 for the subclass 1, and 1 for subclass 2.

For example, if a man or woman is of class C2, we shall say, in our notation, that he or she is of class $(1, 0, 1)$.

Each type of marriage will be designated by a quadruple index (a, b, c, d), where (a, b, c) is the symbol designating the class of the husband, and where d is 0 if the marriage follows formula (I), and 1 if it follows formula (II). Thus, in a marriage $(1, 0, 1, 1)$, the husband is of class $(1, 0, 1)$, that is to say C2, and, the marriage being made according to formula (II), the wife is of class D1, that is to say $(1, 1, 0)$; moreover, the children are of class B1, that is $(0, 1, 0)$.

Generally speaking, in formula (I) marriages, if the husband is of class (a, b, c), the wife is of class $(a, b + 1, c)$; in formula (II) marriages, if the husband is of class (a, b, c), the wife is of class $(a, b + 1, c + 1)$, all this being verified by direct examination of the cases, one by one. Then, in a marriage (a, b, c, d), the husband is of class (a, b, c), and the wife is of class $(a, b + 1, c + d)$.

On the other hand, if the wife is of class (x, y, z), her children are of class $(x + 1, y, x + z + 1)$, this again being verified by direct examination. It follows that, in a marriage (a, b, c, d), the children are of class $(a + 1, b + 1, a + c + d + 1)$.

Now we must make more precise our hypothesis on the alternation between formulae (I) and (II). We shall allow the following four cases: (1) The children always follow the parents' formula; (2) the children always follow the opposite formula to that of the parents, with the result that the formulae will alternate from generation; (3) sons follow the parents' formula, daughters, the opposite of the parents' formula; (4) daughters follow the formula of the parents, and sons the opposite formula. Each one of these cases will be designated by a double index (p, q), as follows: p is 0 if the son follows his parents' formula, case (1) and case (3), and 1 in the contrary case, case (2) and case (4); q is 0 if the daughter follows her parents' formula, case (1) and case (4), and 1 in the contrary case, case (2) and case (3).

That being so, we find, by direct proof from the results obtained above, that the functions f and g previously defined can now be expressed by the following formulae:

$$f(a, b, c, d) \equiv (a + 1, b + 1, a + c + d + 1, d + p) \quad \text{(mod 2)}$$

$$g(a, b, c, d) \equiv (a + 1, b, a + c + q + 1, d + q) \quad \text{(mod 2)}$$

It remains to add that these permutations commute, which means, as we know, that marriage with the daughter of the mother's brother is always permitted. The calculation is easily made and yields:

$$(a, b + 1, c + d + 1) \equiv (a, b + 1, c + d + q + 1) \quad \text{(mod 2)}$$

This shows that q cannot be 1; the cases (2) and (3) are thus excluded by condition (C), and there are no other cases possible except (1) and (4); the first of these latter is the one for a reducible society, composed of two subpopulations of which one always follows marriage formula (I), and the other always follows formula (II). If we leave this case aside, there remains only case (4), where one has $p = 1, q = 0$. The functions f and g are, then:

$$f(a, b, c, d) \equiv (a + 1, b + 1, a + c + d + 1, d + 1) \quad \text{(mod 2)}$$

$$g(a, b, c, d) \equiv (a + 1, b, a + c + 1, d) \quad \text{(mod 2)}$$

By means of these formulae, one can easily submit to calculation all questions relative to this law of marriage. For example, let us ask if marriage with the daughter of the father's sister is possible. In the general case, it is easy to see that one necessary and sufficient condition for this to be possible is that f and g should satisfy the relation $f[f(M_i)] = g[g(M_i)]$. For the law which we have just examined, an immediate calculation shows that this relation is not verified for any choice of the indices, a, b, c, d; thus, no man of the society in question can marry the daughter of his father's sister; an analogous calculation shows that this type of marriage will always be permitted in a society which always applies formula (I) or always formula (II).

Finally, let us find out if the above society is irreducible. There are general methods for treating this type of problem; but here it is easier to note that the combination $b - d$ is "invariant" under the permutations f and g, that is, it has the same value for the symbol with the four indices (a, b, c, d), and for the symbols which result from the permutations f and g respectively. This implies the existence of two distinct subpopulations, the one composed of all the possible combinations of marriages (a, b, c, d) for which $b - d \equiv 0$, that is, $b = d$, and the other including the possible combinations of marriages (a, b, c, d) for which $b - d \equiv 1$, that is, $b \neq d$. In other words, we have here a reducible society which breaks down into these two subpopulations:

1. Men of class A or C, marrying by formula (I).

   Men of class B or D, marrying by formula (II).

   Women of class A or C, marrying by formula (II).

   Women of class B or D, marrying by formula (I).

2. Men of class A or C, marrying by formula (II).

   Men of class B or D, marrying by formula (I).

   Women of class A or C, marrying by formula (I).

   Women of class B or D, marrying by formula (II).

Of course, as we have already noted, these calculations are valuable only if the alternation between formulae (I) and (II) follows one of the simple rules which we have indicated. If this were not so, the calculation would have to be modified; and, if the rules of alternation did not satisfy condition (B), the problem would not be susceptible to treatment by our method.

An Algebraic Treatment of Rules
of Marriage and Descent *

ROBERT R. BUSH

In a number of primitive societies, particularly in Australia, the kinship systems are simple and rigid. Rather specific clans, moieties, generations, etc., are culturally defined for each man, his wife, and his children. This permits us to distinguish a specified number of possible *marriage types* and to deduce from the ethnographic material the allowed marriage type of a man or woman when we know the marriage type of his or her parents. When the rules of marriage and descent are sufficiently specific and unique we might expect to describe the system mathematically. Whether or not such a description is useful remains to be seen.

Let us begin with a simple example. In the *Kariera system*, four classes or submoieties are defined. These are known as Banaka, Burung, Palyori, and Karimera; let us label them A, B, C, and D, respectively. Now the rules of marriage are:

(1) an A man marries a B woman.

(2) a B man marries an A woman.

(3) a C man marries a D woman.

(4) a D man marries a C woman.

* This is an extension of A. Weil's appendix to the first part of C. Lévi-Strauss, *Les Structures Elementaires de la Parente*. (Paris: Presses Universitaires de France, 1949). I am indebted to Professor G. C. Homans for the empirical material. (R. R. Bush).

We shall refer to these as marriage types 1, 2, 3, 4, respectively. Moreover, the rules of descent are:

(a) the child of an A man is a C.
(b) the child of a B man is a D.
(c) the child of a C man is an A.
(d) the child of a D man is a B.

Without using any mathematics, we see at once that the son from marriage type 1 must contract a marriage of type 3 while the daughter from marriage type 1 must enter into a marriage of type 4, etc. In fact, we can construct the following table:

marriage type of parents	1	2	3	4
marriage type of son	3	4	1	2
marriage type of daughters	4	3	2	1

With the information given we can carry the inferences a generation further to obtain the following table:

parents	1	2	3	4
son	3	4	1	2
son's son	1	2	3	4
son's daughter	2	1	4	3
daughter	4	3	2	1
daughter's son	2	1	4	3
daughter's daughter	1	2	3	4

Thus we see that my son's son must contract the same marriage type as my daughter's daughter. Hence, my son's son *could* marry my daughter's daughter. This is equivalent to saying that a man can marry his father's sister's daughter. Moreover, from the above table we see that my son's daughter can marry my daughter's son, i.e., that a man may marry his mother's brother's daughter. These cross-cousin marriages are in fact permitted in Kariera.

So far we have not used any mathematics although the reasoning has been somewhat mathematical. We see from the above tables that if we begin with a sequence, 1 2 3 4, further entries in the table are merely permutations of that sequence, e.g., 3 4 1 2. This suggests at once the kind of mathematics which is appropriate, viz., the algebra of permutations or special topics in group theory, matrix algebra, or operator algebra. I shall introduce the necessary mathematical tools as we go along, but first let's formalize the characteristics of the types of kinship systems we are discussing.

Following Weil, we make the following two basic assumptions:

I. For every individual there is precisely one type of marriage which he or she may contract.

II. For every individual the type of marriage which he or she may contract depends only upon (a) his or her sex, and (b) the type of marriage of his or her parents.

For analytic purposes, we divide a society into N *classes* which are mutually exclusive and exhaustive. Each member of the society, then, is in one and only one of these classes. Moreover, he or she may choose a spouse from one and only one of these N classes and their sons will belong to one specified class and their daughters will belong to another or the same specified class. Note that the example of the Kariera discussed above fits these requirements.

Throughout the following discussion we shall be using the concept of a mathematical *operator*. In particular we shall be concerned with *permutation operators* which operate on a sequence of numbers or letters in such a way that a new permutation of those symbols is obtained. For example, if we have a sequence (123) and a permutation operator P we could write

(1) $$P(123) = (231).$$

This equation should be read "P operating on the sequence (123) gives the sequence (231)." Other permutations are possible, of course; in fact there are six in all. Thus, there are six possible permutation operators when the *operand* is a sequence of three symbols. Permutation operators may be represented by a special class of matrices which are called, curiously enough, *permutation matrices*. If we have a set of three symbols, the permutation matrix is a 3×3 matrix which contains one and only one "1" in each row and column and has zeros elsewhere. The operand, which we denote by x, is written as a column vector. For the above example the operand is

(2) $$x = \begin{bmatrix} 1 \\ 2 \\ 3 \end{bmatrix},$$

and the matrix operator is

(3) $$P = \begin{bmatrix} 0 & 1 & 0 \\ 0 & 0 & 1 \\ 1 & 0 & 0 \end{bmatrix},$$

and by the rule of matrix multiplication we obtain

(4) $$Px = \begin{bmatrix} 0 & 1 & 0 \\ 0 & 0 & 1 \\ 1 & 0 & 0 \end{bmatrix} \begin{bmatrix} 1 \\ 2 \\ 3 \end{bmatrix} = \begin{bmatrix} 2 \\ 3 \\ 1 \end{bmatrix},$$

in agreement with Eq. (1). The six possible 3×3 permutation matrices and the vectors they produce when applied to x of Eq. (2) are shown below.

P	Px	P	Px
$\begin{bmatrix} 1 & 0 & 0 \\ 0 & 1 & 0 \\ 0 & 0 & 1 \end{bmatrix}$	$\begin{bmatrix} 1 \\ 2 \\ 3 \end{bmatrix}$	$\begin{bmatrix} 0 & 0 & 1 \\ 0 & 1 & 0 \\ 1 & 0 & 0 \end{bmatrix}$	$\begin{bmatrix} 3 \\ 2 \\ 1 \end{bmatrix}$
$\begin{bmatrix} 1 & 0 & 0 \\ 0 & 0 & 1 \\ 0 & 1 & 0 \end{bmatrix}$	$\begin{bmatrix} 1 \\ 3 \\ 2 \end{bmatrix}$	$\begin{bmatrix} 0 & 1 & 0 \\ 0 & 0 & 1 \\ 1 & 0 & 0 \end{bmatrix}$	$\begin{bmatrix} 2 \\ 3 \\ 1 \end{bmatrix}$
$\begin{bmatrix} 0 & 1 & 0 \\ 1 & 0 & 0 \\ 0 & 0 & 1 \end{bmatrix}$	$\begin{bmatrix} 2 \\ 1 \\ 3 \end{bmatrix}$	$\begin{bmatrix} 0 & 0 & 1 \\ 1 & 0 & 0 \\ 0 & 1 & 0 \end{bmatrix}$	$\begin{bmatrix} 3 \\ 1 \\ 2 \end{bmatrix}$

In general we shall have M symbols and will then have $M!$ different $M \times M$ matrix operators. Each will produce a new permutation of the M symbols. One of these $M!$ matrices will be the *identity operator I* which does not change the sequence. Its matrix will have "1's" along the main diagonal.

We shall make use of a theorem from the theory of groups. This theorem says that if A is a member of a *cyclic group* there exists some positive integer n, called the order of the group, such that

$$A^n = I.$$

This theorem may require some amplification. First of all, our permutation operators do form what is called a cyclic group. Secondly, the notation A^n means, for our purposes, the operator A applied n times. The theorem then tells us that if we apply A repeatedly for n times we will obtain the identity operator I. Moreover, it is known from group theory that n is never larger than the number of elements in the vector operand. In other words, if X contains M symbols, then for any of our $M \times M$ matrices P, we have

$$P^n = I \qquad (n = 1, 2, \ldots, M).$$

This will be a useful theorem, as we shall see presently.

One further concept from operator algebra before we go on: two operators A and B are said to *commute* if we have

$$AB = BA.$$

In other words, A and B commute if we obtain the same result when we apply B first and A next to an operand as when we apply A first and then B. (If two operators commute they are members of an abelian group). Not all of our permutation operators will commute with another but some will, as we shall see.

We now return to our discussion of kinship systems. We define M types of marriages and label them in arbitrary order, X_1, X_2, ..., X_M. These M types form a column vector,

$$X = \begin{bmatrix} X_1 \\ X_2 \\ \cdot \\ \cdot \\ \cdot \\ X_M \end{bmatrix},$$

which, to save space, we shall frequently write as $[X_1 X_2 \cdots X_M]$. Now the son from a marriage of type X_i, where $i = 1, 2, \ldots, M$, may contract a marriage of type X_i'. These X_i' form another column vector,

$$X' = \begin{bmatrix} X_1' \\ X_2' \\ \cdot \\ \cdot \\ \cdot \\ X_M' \end{bmatrix},$$

which we also denote by $[X_1' X_2' \cdots X_M']$. To obtain the vector X' from the vector X we need an operator F defined by

$$FX = X'.$$

The operator F is a permutation operator representable by an $M \times M$ matrix. The rules of marriage and descent of the society will specify F.

Similarly, the daughter from a marriage of type X_i must contract a marriage of type X_1'' and the set of X_1'' form a vector

$$X'' = \begin{bmatrix} X_1'' \\ X_2'' \\ \cdot \\ \cdot \\ \cdot \\ X_M'' \end{bmatrix},$$

which we also write as $(X_1'' X_2'' \cdots X_M'')$. To obtain X'' from X we need an operator G defined by

$$GX = X''$$

The operator G may also be represented by an $M \times M$ matrix. The kinship chart (Fig. A2.1) may help clarify the meaning of the operators.

We may now translate our introductory discussion of Kariera into our newly acquired terminology. The four types of marriage are X_1, X_2, X_3, X_4

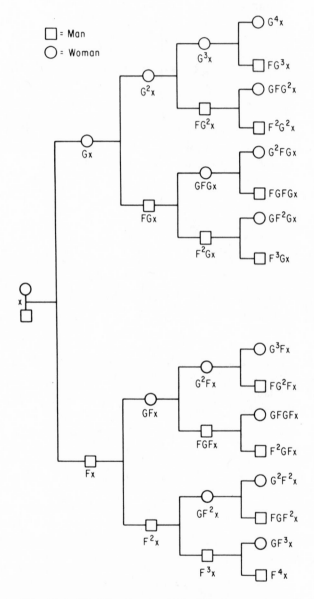

Fig. A2.1. Kinship diagram indicating the meanings of the various combinations of the operators F and G. The operations shown indicate the marriage type which the person may contract.

and form the vector $[X_1 X_2 X_3 X_4]$. The operators F and G are given by the matrices

$$F = \begin{bmatrix} 0 & 0 & 1 & 0 \\ 0 & 0 & 0 & 1 \\ 1 & 0 & 0 & 0 \\ 0 & 1 & 0 & 0 \end{bmatrix}, \qquad G = \begin{bmatrix} 0 & 0 & 0 & 1 \\ 0 & 0 & 1 & 0 \\ 0 & 1 & 0 & 0 \\ 1 & 0 & 0 & 0 \end{bmatrix}$$

By applying F and G to the vector $X = [X_1 \ X_2 \ X_3 \ X_4]$ we obtain

$$FX = \begin{bmatrix} 0 & 0 & 1 & 0 \\ 0 & 0 & 0 & 1 \\ 1 & 0 & 0 & 0 \\ 0 & 1 & 0 & 0 \end{bmatrix} \begin{bmatrix} X_1 \\ X_2 \\ X_3 \\ X_4 \end{bmatrix} = \begin{bmatrix} X_3 \\ X_4 \\ X_1 \\ X_2 \end{bmatrix},$$

$$GX = \begin{bmatrix} 0 & 0 & 0 & 1 \\ 0 & 0 & 1 & 0 \\ 0 & 1 & 0 & 0 \\ 1 & 0 & 0 & 0 \end{bmatrix} \begin{bmatrix} X_1 \\ X_2 \\ X_3 \\ X_4 \end{bmatrix} = \begin{bmatrix} X_4 \\ X_3 \\ X_2 \\ X_1 \end{bmatrix}.$$

Indeed, we obtain on the right the sequences of numbers presented in the tables above.

Next let's compute some matrix products, not just because it's fun but also because we shall use them shortly. The product of F times itself is

$$F^2 = \begin{bmatrix} 0 & 0 & 1 & 0 \\ 0 & 0 & 0 & 1 \\ 1 & 0 & 0 & 0 \\ 0 & 1 & 0 & 0 \end{bmatrix} \begin{bmatrix} 0 & 0 & 1 & 0 \\ 0 & 0 & 0 & 1 \\ 1 & 0 & 0 & 0 \\ 0 & 1 & 0 & 0 \end{bmatrix} = \begin{bmatrix} 1 & 0 & 0 & 0 \\ 0 & 1 & 0 & 0 \\ 0 & 0 & 1 & 0 \\ 0 & 0 & 0 & 1 \end{bmatrix} = I$$

The product of G times itself is

$$G^2 = \begin{bmatrix} 0 & 0 & 0 & 1 \\ 0 & 0 & 1 & 0 \\ 0 & 1 & 0 & 0 \\ 1 & 0 & 0 & 0 \end{bmatrix} \begin{bmatrix} 0 & 0 & 0 & 1 \\ 0 & 0 & 1 & 0 \\ 0 & 1 & 0 & 0 \\ 1 & 0 & 0 & 0 \end{bmatrix} = \begin{bmatrix} 1 & 0 & 0 & 0 \\ 0 & 1 & 0 & 0 \\ 0 & 0 & 1 & 0 \\ 0 & 0 & 0 & 1 \end{bmatrix} = I.$$

We conclude then that both F applied twice and G applied twice are equivalent to applying the identity operator. What does this mean in kinship English? Simply that I (a man) am of the same class as my father's father and my son's son, or that I (a woman) am of the same class as my mother's mother and my daughter's daughter. These statements are true of Kariera if not amazing. Let's proceed. The products of F and G are

$$FG = \begin{bmatrix} 0 & 0 & 1 & 0 \\ 0 & 0 & 0 & 1 \\ 1 & 0 & 0 & 0 \\ 0 & 1 & 0 & 0 \end{bmatrix} \begin{bmatrix} 0 & 0 & 0 & 1 \\ 0 & 0 & 1 & 0 \\ 0 & 1 & 0 & 0 \\ 1 & 0 & 0 & 0 \end{bmatrix} = \begin{bmatrix} 0 & 1 & 0 & 0 \\ 1 & 0 & 0 & 0 \\ 0 & 0 & 0 & 1 \\ 0 & 0 & 1 & 0 \end{bmatrix},$$

$$GF = \begin{bmatrix} 0 & 0 & 0 & 1 \\ 0 & 0 & 1 & 0 \\ 0 & 1 & 0 & 0 \\ 1 & 0 & 0 & 0 \end{bmatrix} \begin{bmatrix} 0 & 0 & 1 & 0 \\ 0 & 0 & 0 & 1 \\ 1 & 0 & 0 & 0 \\ 0 & 1 & 0 & 0 \end{bmatrix} = \begin{bmatrix} 0 & 1 & 0 & 0 \\ 1 & 0 & 0 & 0 \\ 0 & 0 & 0 & 1 \\ 0 & 0 & 1 & 0 \end{bmatrix}.$$

And so we see that F and G commute, i.e.,

$$FG = GF.$$

What does this imply? Simply that my daughter's son and my son's daughter may contract the same type of marriage and hence may marry one another. This is to say that a man may marry his mother's brother's daughter or a woman may marry her father's sister's son. (Compare the simplicity of these statements with the statement "F and G commute.")

One last computation for Kariera: the square of the product $FG = GF$ is

$$(FG)^2 = (GF)^2 = \begin{bmatrix} 0 & 1 & 0 & 0 \\ 1 & 0 & 0 & 0 \\ 0 & 0 & 0 & 1 \\ 0 & 0 & 1 & 0 \end{bmatrix} \begin{bmatrix} 0 & 1 & 0 & 0 \\ 1 & 0 & 0 & 0 \\ 0 & 0 & 0 & 1 \\ 0 & 0 & 1 & 0 \end{bmatrix}$$

$$= \begin{bmatrix} 1 & 0 & 0 & 0 \\ 0 & 1 & 0 & 0 \\ 0 & 0 & 1 & 0 \\ 0 & 0 & 0 & 1 \end{bmatrix} = I.$$

We may write this result in the form

$$FGFG = GFGF = I.$$

The interpretation: I belong to the same class as my daughter's son's daughter's son if I am a man or to my son's daughter's son's daughter if I am a woman. Of course, my daughter's son's daughter's son may marry my son's daughter's son's daughter. I say "of course" since F and G commute, implying that my daughter's son may marry my son's daughter.

As a second example of a four-class society I will discuss the system in Tarau. The four classes are called Pochana, Tlangsha, Thimasha, and Khuipu. For ease in pronunciation, we call these A, B, C, and D, respectively. The rules of marriage and descent are summarized as follows:

an A man marries a B woman and has A children.

a B man marries a C woman and has B children.

a C man marries a D woman and has C children.

a D man marries an A woman and has D children.

We denote these marriage types by the vector $X = [X_1 X_2 X_3 X_4]$ and can deduce that the "son" and "daughter" operators are

$$F = \begin{bmatrix} 1 & 0 & 0 & 0 \\ 0 & 1 & 0 & 0 \\ 0 & 0 & 1 & 0 \\ 0 & 0 & 0 & 1 \end{bmatrix} = I,$$

and

$$G = \begin{bmatrix} 0 & 0 & 0 & 1 \\ 1 & 0 & 0 & 0 \\ 0 & 1 & 0 & 0 \\ 0 & 0 & 1 & 0 \end{bmatrix}.$$

A child is always of the same class as his or her father. Hence, if the child is male he must contract the same type of marriage as his parents. Hence, F is the identity operator I. Since the identity operator I commutes with all other operators, F and G commute, i.e.,

$$FG = GF,$$

and so cross-cousin marriage is permissible.

We now compute some products of G with itself. The square is

$$G^2 = \begin{bmatrix} 0 & 0 & 0 & 1 \\ 1 & 0 & 0 & 0 \\ 0 & 1 & 0 & 0 \\ 0 & 0 & 1 & 0 \end{bmatrix} \begin{bmatrix} 0 & 0 & 0 & 1 \\ 1 & 0 & 0 & 0 \\ 0 & 1 & 0 & 0 \\ 0 & 0 & 1 & 0 \end{bmatrix} = \begin{bmatrix} 0 & 0 & 1 & 0 \\ 0 & 0 & 0 & 1 \\ 1 & 0 & 0 & 0 \\ 0 & 1 & 0 & 0 \end{bmatrix}.$$

We know from the theorem about cyclic groups stated above that for some positive integer $n \leq 4$ we have

$$G^n = I.$$

We wish to discover the value of n for Tarau's operator G. So we compute the cube of G:

$$G^3 = GG^2 = \begin{bmatrix} 0 & 0 & 0 & 1 \\ 1 & 0 & 0 & 0 \\ 0 & 1 & 0 & 0 \\ 0 & 0 & 1 & 0 \end{bmatrix} \begin{bmatrix} 0 & 0 & 1 & 0 \\ 0 & 0 & 0 & 1 \\ 1 & 0 & 0 & 0 \\ 0 & 1 & 0 & 0 \end{bmatrix} = \begin{bmatrix} 0 & 1 & 0 & 0 \\ 0 & 0 & 1 & 0 \\ 0 & 0 & 0 & 1 \\ 1 & 0 & 0 & 0 \end{bmatrix}.$$

We still do not have the identity matrix I and so we compute G^4. (This must equal I according to our theorem):

$$G^4 = GG^3 = \begin{bmatrix} 0 & 0 & 0 & 1 \\ 1 & 0 & 0 & 0 \\ 0 & 1 & 0 & 0 \\ 0 & 0 & 1 & 0 \end{bmatrix} \begin{bmatrix} 0 & 1 & 0 & 0 \\ 0 & 0 & 1 & 0 \\ 0 & 0 & 0 & 1 \\ 1 & 0 & 0 & 0 \end{bmatrix} = \begin{bmatrix} 1 & 0 & 0 & 0 \\ 0 & 1 & 0 & 0 \\ 0 & 0 & 1 & 0 \\ 0 & 0 & 0 & 1 \end{bmatrix} = I.$$

And so we find at last,

$$G^4 = I.$$

This equation asserts that in Tarau my daughter's daughter's daughter's daughter must contract the same type of marriage as I have.

Now that we have discussed two examples for the case of $M = 4$ types of marriage, we shall be a bit more systematic. We shall consider all possible operators for the cases of $M = 2, 3,$ and 4 and hence will obtain a broader framework for discussing special cases.

When we have only two types of permitted marriage ($M = 2$) we have only two operators:

$$P_1 = \begin{bmatrix} 1 & 0 \\ 0 & 1 \end{bmatrix}, \qquad P_2 = \begin{bmatrix} 0 & 1 \\ 1 & 0 \end{bmatrix}.$$

P_1 is the identity operator and P_2 merely interchange X_1 and X_2 in the vector operand $[X_1 X_2]$. These two operators commute and we have the relation

$$P_2^2 = I = P_1.$$

When we have three types of marriage, X_1, X_2, and X_3, we have $3! = 6$ possible operators. These may be defined by the following equations:

$$P_1 X = [1 \ \ 2 \ \ 3],$$
$$P_2 X = [1 \ \ 3 \ \ 2],$$
$$P_3 X = [2 \ \ 1 \ \ 3],$$
$$P_4 X = [3 \ \ 2 \ \ 1],$$
$$P_5 X = [2 \ \ 3 \ \ 1],$$
$$P_6 X = [3 \ \ 1 \ \ 2].$$

Powers of these operators which lead to the identity operator I are shown by the following relations:

$$P_1 = I,$$
$$P_2^2 = P_3^2 = P_4^2 = I,$$
$$P_5^3 = P_6^3 = I.$$

Of course P_1 commutes with all the other operators, but P_2, P_3, and P_4 do not commute with one another (pairwise). The last two operators do commute:

$$P_5 P_6 = P_6 P_5 = I.$$

All possible pairwise combinations of the six operators lead to the multiplication table shown below.

First operator in product

	P_1	P_2	P_3	P_4	P_5	P_6
P_1	I	P_2	P_3	P_4	P_5	P_6
P_2	P_2	I	P_6	P_5	P_4	P_3
P_3	P_3	P_5	I	P_6	P_2	P_4
P_4	P_4	P_6	P_5	I	P_3	P_2
P_5	P_5	P_3	P_4	P_2	P_6	I
P_6	P_6	P_4	P_2	P_3	I	P_5

I have been unable to find any examples of societies with three marriage types and so we proceed to the case of $M = 4$.

When four types of marriage exist ($M = 4$), there are $4! = 24$ possible operators, corresponding to the 24 permutations of four symbols. These 24 operators may be divided into four groups depending on the value of n in the relation $P^n = I$. In the first group ($n = 1$) we have only the identity operator, I. In the second group ($n = 2$) we have nine operators; six of these always leave two of the indices unchanged in position while the remaining three change the position of all four indices. In the third group ($n = 3$) we have eight operators, and each of these leaves one index unchanged. The fourth group ($n = 4$) contains six operators, each of which changes the position of all four indices. The operators F and G for the example of Kariera discussed above are in the second group. The operator G for Tarau is in the fourth group. Shown in the following table are the results of each of the 24 operators operating on the vector $X = [X_1 X_2 X_3 X_4]$ which we abbreviate for this purpose by [1 2 3 4].

	Px	P^2x	P^3x	P^4x
$n = 1$	1234			
$n = 2$	1243	I		
	1324	I		
	1432	I		
	2134	I		
	3214	I		
	4231	I		
	2143	I		
	3412	I		
	4321	I		
$n = 3$	1423	1342	I	
	1342	1423	I	
	2314	3124	I	
	3124	2314	I	
	4132	2431	I	
	2431	4132	I	
	3241	4213	I	
	4213	3241	I	
	2341	3412	4123	I
	4123	3412	2341	I
	2413	4321	3142	I
	3142	4321	2413	I
	3421	2143	4312	I
	4312	2143	3421	I

Problem for an ambitious student: Work out the 24 × 24 "multiplication table" for these 24 operators, analogous to the one given above for the $M = 3$ case.

One can easily see that the number of possible operators is getting large too rapidly for us to continue enumerating cases. When $M = 5$ we have $5! = 120$ possible operators. Moreover, each kinship system has two operators and so there are $(M!)^2$ possible systems.

In spite of the great number of possible systems, we shall consider a single example of a more complex system, that of Aranda. There are eight classes as listed below:

Marriage type	Man	Woman	Children
1	A1	B1	D2
2	A2	B2	D1
3	B1	A1	C1
4	B2	A2	C2
5	C2	D2	B2
6	C1	D1	B1
7	D1	C1	A2
8	D2	C2	A1

Types 5 and 6 have not been reversed unintentionally as one might suspect. Note that the sequence A1, A2, B1, etc., under man is inverted under children. The operators F and G are defined by

$$FX = [8\ 7\ 6\ 5\ 4\ 3\ 2\ 1],$$

$$GX = [5\ 6\ 7\ 8\ 2\ 1\ 4\ 3],$$

These operators can be shown to have the following properties:

$$F^2 = I,$$

$$G^4 = I,$$

$$(GF)^2 = (FG)^2 = I.$$

From these properties we can deduce an important rule. From the first property we have

$$IG = F^2G = GI = GF^2,$$

or

$$FFG = GFF.$$

This relation says that my daughter's son's son may marry my son's son's daughter, i.e., that a man may marry his father's mother's brother's son's daughter. This is one of the rules of Aranda marriage.

From the properties $(FG)^2 = I$ and $F^2 = I$ we obtain

$$FGFG = I = (F^2)^2,$$

or

$$FGFG = FF^3,$$

or

$$GFG = FFF.$$

This result implies that my daughter's son's daughter may marry my son's son's son, i.e., that a woman may marry her father's mother's brother's son's son. This is the other part of the Aranda marriage rule.

From the properties $G^4 = I$ and $(GF)^2 = I$ we obtain

$$GFGF = G^4,$$

or

$$FGF = GGG,$$

and this says that a man can marry his mother's father's sister's daughter's daughter.

We conclude by raising three general questions:

1. What are the conditions which permit cross-cousin marriage?

2. What are the conditions which permit parallel-cousin marriage?

3. What are the conditions which permit a man to marry his father's mother's brother's son's daughter and a woman to marry her father's mother's brother's son's son, as in Aranda?

The answer to the first question was implicitly answered in the preceding examples. The condition for a man to marry his mother's brother's daughter or for a girl to marry her father's sister's son is

$$FG = GF,$$

while the condition for a man to marry his father's sister's daughter or for a woman to marry her mother's brother's son is

$$F^2 = G^2.$$

The answer to the second question is also simple. For a man to marry his mother's sister's daughter or for a woman to marry her mother's sister's son we must have

$$FG = G^2,$$

while for a man to marry his father's brother's daughter or for a woman to marry her father's brother's son, we must have

$$GF = F^2,$$

but each of these two relations implies that

$$F = G.$$

If this condition is met then a man may also marry his own sister!

The answer to the third question is more involved. We have given that

$$FFG = GFF \quad \text{and} \quad GFG = FFF.$$

There are several solutions to these equations including

(a) $F = G$,

(b) $G = I, F^2 = I$,

(c) $F = I, G^2 = I$,

(d) $F^2 = I, (FG)^2 = I$ (as in Aranda),

(e) $FG = GF, G^2 = F^2$.

Undoubtedly other solutions also exist.

Index

173